Tommy Dee

Confessions of a Taxi Driver

europe books

© 2021 **Europe Books**| London
www.europebooks.co.uk | info@europebooks.co.uk

ISBN 9791220117852
First edition: December 2021
Distribution for the United Kingdom: **Vine House
Distribution ltd**

Printed for Italy by Rotomail Italia
Finito di stampare presso Rotomail Italia S.p.A. - Vignate (MI)

Confessions of a Taxi Driver

To all those that played their part in making this book possible, and to my family who showed me the value of life.

The Base

To grasp the reality of promiscuity or the decadence of society, you must see it first-hand, witness the shocking immoral and degenerate lifestyle that for some was the norm.

In the early eighties, driving a Taxi around Dublin was an education like no other, a profession that brings you into a world of drugs, brothels, prostitution, violence and infidelity, where, in an average night, a passenger could vomit, masturbate, coke-up, or have sex in your car, where it was nothing unusual to have your head punched-in, or end up running across fields trying to catch your fare high on ecstasy, inhaling their body odours, submerged in a world of perversion and debauchery.

For those who lived it, they first got accustomed to it, then desensitised, until it became their normality. Driving a Taxi you unconsciously become an absorbing sponge for your passengers, as they reveal their innermost secrets to a total stranger, seeking absolution or understanding. With each fare, the Taxi Driver changes his views and opinions like a starfish to avoid confrontation, while the smart ones try at least to act like moral compasses; their behaviour, the result of getting diluted over the years with every generation, the young ones always thinking the older generation hasn't got a clue of life.

This book will certainly change that view as it is about Taxi Drivers and their passengers in the eighties and nighties, their exploits, and the bizarre and mystifying lives they lived. And yes, it's all true, only names and places have been changed to protect their privacy and some scenes have been created from dramatic purpose.

A Base, for a Taxi company is where the radio controller is located; he takes the incoming calls on the phone from potential passengers and then selects the closest taxi rank to the address or the nearest taxi if there isn't any available at the Taxi Rank. Normally, he would give out jobs and assistance, but for a Taxi Driver he is a companion in the car, a confessional or an alibi maker, the voice which turns a mundane night into something memorable. In the early eighties, most Base Controllers were former Taxi Drivers who lost their licences for drink driving or for some violent acts.

They knew all too well the sins of the Taxi business: pussy, drink, and gambling. Instinctually, they could read a situation and knew what needed to be done, get on the wrong side of them, and they could make your life hell. John O Shea was a former Taxi Driver, thirty-seven, his vice was pussy.

Having seven women on the go, he eventually got caught when three got pregnant, and the others got syphilis. Surrounded by a harem of women while their brothers were constantly trying to cut his dick off, after some time, he stopped driving.

The biggest temptation in the Taxi Business is women as no other job allows you to bring home lonely and sometimes horny women. Every night, inhibitions removed, usually after a night of alcohol; for the young Taxi Driver it was a candy store of sex, swinging, orgy's, threesomes, blowjobs, and hand jobs.

The story starts in December 1981, Kilmore Taxi's Base was located in Coolock on Dublin's Northside, it

10

had eighteen Taxi Drivers who all had earned their nicknames for obvious reasons, John, the Base Controller, was called "Pulse" because he would fuck anything with one.

It was Friday night, one of the busiest nights back then, John, high on weed was joking with his best friend Driver "69" known as Gorgeous George, 26 stunningly attractive, athletic, with piercing, blue eyes, and hung like a donkey according to his female passengers that waited on taxi ranks for him to arrive; sometimes, queuing for over an hour for him. George and John had a great bro relationship, too often John would go missing for two or three hours, most thought he had fallen asleep, but the truth was he hooked up with George and ended up in a flat near the Base for fucking passengers called "The Garage."

John came up with the idea to rent a flat for himself, and while he was at work, he would rent it out by the hour to any Taxi Driver who needed a place to fuck. It was a fiver an hour and an extra quid for a condom. Most weekends, he would make more money from the flat, than he did working, ridiculing any driver over the airwaves who didn't clean up after themselves or who went overtime or even those that left very early. He rented an adjoining flat for Taxi Drivers who got fucked out by their wives, charging them thirty quid a week. Part of the agreement was he could rent out the rooms when they were at work unless they scored themselves.

The Jonah, Driver 6

Poor Peter, every Taxi company had one, an unfortunate individual everything just seemed to happen to.

He was in his late fifties, quiet spoken, and a devout catholic with a stereotypical accountant persona; every mannerism he displayed, alien to any typical Dublin Taxi Driver at that time. Poor Peter was forced to drive a Taxi around Dublin due to redundancy, his accent too refined for 99% of his passengers, sounding more like a judge than a Dublin cabbie.

John, the Base controller, absolutely loved to take the piss out of him at least once during his shift. Sadly, Peter was seriously short on street smarts and fell for Johns pranks every time.

On Peter's first night driving a Taxi, John sent him to a brothel looking to collect an exercise instructor called Miss Cuminaflood, asking Peter if he had a big boot as she had a lot of luggage that might need to be, John stressing the word *strapped on.*

"She might give you *a hand* if you're lucky," John's laughter filling the airwaves along with the other drivers.

According to Bab's, a very large black woman who practised dominatrix in the Brothel, known to most Taxi Drivers from collecting or bringing male clients for a service, Peter was totally clueless.

He knocked on the door, and in a very posh voice said: "I'm looking for Miss Cuminaflood." Babs, joined in on the prank as John had phoned the brothel before Peter arrived. Babs asked Peter to repeat the name slowly, "A Miss Cum- in –a- flood" Peter replied, "She's an exercise instructor."

Babs opened the steel door allowing Peter to walk into the dimly lit room that smelled like a combination of mildew and cheap perfume. After the steel door slammed closed, she leaned across Peter and slid the large deadbolt back. Babs, wearing her crotchless and ass-less PVC suit and with her very large size 40 double D's hanging out, suddenly started rubbing off on Peter's starched white shirt. Peter, on the other hand was glowing redder by the second as he tried to look away from her tits, blessing himself over and over, under his breath, *repeating the rosary*. Then, other naked girls made their appearance in the room, joining the prank and asking Miss Cuminaflood if she was ready.

At that point, Peter stuttering said, "I think I'm at the wrong address." But the girls surrounded him, and began caressing his crotch, squeezing his balls, and after placing a necklace made of condoms around his neck, they started simulating a Hawaiian dance and saying, "Aloha, we are here for your pleasure."

One of the girls grabbed his hand and stroked another girls' tits with it. Then, she said "You touchy the booby you pay the money."

Peter shouted, "I'm married, I'm married," just as a punter walked out of a servicing room, he turned to Peter and said, "Aren't we fucking all mate?" The door opened to let the punter out and Peter ran out, jumped in his taxi, locked the doors and screamed into the hand piece of his radio, "Driver 6, I'm being raped."

John called the code across the airwaves, "Driver 6 is having a Charlie," Charlie was code for serious assault, "He is outside Tandies on South Great George's Street."

John asked Peter if he was alright, and with heavy breathing Peter replied, "Am I alright? a group of fucking degenerate nymphomaniacs were swinging out of my genitals." John's reply was typical of his twisted sense of humour. "What's a nymphomaniac Peter, is that someone who compulsively steals stuff? I think me Ma was one of them." Peter was still in a frenzy, and still screaming he howled again, "A huge black woman dressed in a plastic and much revealing costume answered the door," to which John repeated for all to hear in a feigned shocked voice, "A big black woman with her bits hanging out tried to put you into a plastic bag, was it a big bag Peter?"

With the Taxi radio in each car turned up, every driver and their passengers could hear what was going on,-most of them laughing and enjoying the comedy.

Unfortunately, Driver 22 Buckets of Blood had just picked up the parish priest from Templeogue with his elderly mother. Buckets was a few sandwiches short of a picnic, with a quick aggressive violent temper and a deep hatred towards the clergy; the result of having been abused when he was a kid. The decision of sending Buckets to pick them up meant that John's twisted sense of humour was at play again, so it came as no surprise that in the moment the priest asked Buckets, "Could you possibly switch that filth off?"

Buckets replied in his gruff deep Dublin dialect, "Fuckoff and don't tell me what to do, you fucking pervert." He turned up the volume on the radio higher, both the priest and his mother froze and said, "Can we get out of here?" Buckets even more annoyed as he had only travelled a couple of hundred yards with them, simply turned around, and his menacing face full of scars and teeth missing had to be enough as, they said together, "It's okay, it's okay, that's fine, carry-on."

As drivers appeared outside Tandies to help Driver 6, the stage was set for John to have fun, so he continued replying to the drivers, "Naked women were groping Driver 6, that's our driver Peter, stressing heavily," "Ahh poor Peter, that's terrible, what's this world coming to when a Taxi Driver is being pulled off? Sorry, I meant to say groped in broad daylight." Other drivers on the scene wanted to join in.

Driver 33, aka the Hump, formerly known as Quasimodo because of his deformed back, every time someone called him Quasimodo he got the hump so, in the end, the name stuck. The Hump asked, "John, Driver 6 is wearing a condom chain around his neck, is that part of the new taxi uniform?"

John replied, "Are they used condoms Driver 33?" followed very quickly by the lyrics of Frankie Goes to Hollywood, "Relax, don't do it, when you want to go to it, relax, don't do it, when you want to come."

John chastised some creative driver for playing that across the Airwaves "Ahh come off it lads, that's not nice," which led to a barrage of comments, all related to Peter probably looking for some form of compensation for trauma and shock after being subjected to such disturbing images. Some of the drivers even asked John to start a fund so Peter would get some occupational physical therapy, nominating Tandies for a discounted hand relief, pointing out there was no sense in them offering Peter a blowjob because he more than likely thought that was another form of employment and would have to declare it, to the revenue.

Driver 9, "Ram Jam"

Driver 9, known as Ram Jam, was always high on something, paranoid, and had a terrible hatred for black men after one of them fucked off with his wife.

Ram Jam's other job was selling soft and hard drugs along with pimping out some girls. John, who financially benefited from Ram Jam had another set of code words for him: weed was called *motor oil*, coke was *jump leads*, ecstasy was *sparkplugs,* uppers were *petrol,* and the girls were *tyres.* Most of the other drivers hadn't a clue and thought Ram Jam was running a car parts shop on the side.

Viagra wasn't heard of back in the early eighties and John, being an entrepreneur, had his own unique network, selling Dewitt's tablets normally used for kidney issues, he named *steelies* for erectile dysfunction, which had some strange side-effects, and rabbit shite he sold as Moroccan Black, which he cultivated from his pet rabbits and wrapped in Cadbury's tinfoil for authenticity and called it *black magic.*

Most of the younger Taxi Drivers were asked every night for either drugs or prostitutes; it was a readymade market with a perfect supply chain.

Ram Jam would deliberately park outside Dublin's night clubs known for black patrons, Lord Johns and Barbarella's waiting for his prey. Barbarella's was located down a lane just off Baggot Street, Ram Jam would siphon petrol from their cars, another product he sold, and then when they broke down or the cars wouldn't start, he would pick them up. That was the start of their journey to Hell.

That particular night, Driver 28 Kieran, known as ET because he never went home, was parked behind Ram Jam outside Barbarella's at four am. Not familiar with Ram Jam, Kieran got out the car, walked up, and knocked on Ram Jams window.

Ram Jam reacted by jumping out, putting a knife to Kieran's neck, and shouted, "You fucking Black bastard!" Kieran nearly shitted himself screaming "I'm a Taxi Man, I'm a Taxi Man!" Ram Jam, noticing Kieran's Taxi badge and his face drained of colour, said in his adopted Jamaican accent, "You shouldn't be sneaking up on me boy, I could've slashed your ass."

Kieran was now slowly walking backwards to his Taxi, but before he returned to it, Ram Jam asked him if he wanted some cheap Petrol. And, since Kieran wanted to save money, he reluctantly answered, "Yes."

Ram Jam opened his boot which contained five eight-gallon drums of petrol he had siphoned earlier, and after placing one drum on the roof of ET's car, he started sucking hard on the tube filled with petrol, directing the liquid straight into ET's petrol tank. After that, Kieran asked Ram Jam where he got the Petrol from, and Ram jam replied, "Don't be fucking asking me questions boy," raising the knife again, "I be shanking you." Kieran was petrified, so he quickly paid him and got back into his car.

Shortly afterwards, a group of five people came out of the club, three black guys and two white girls, who got into a Ford Capri beside ET'S and turned over the engine, which started straight away but quickly died.

One of the guys got out and checked his petrol cap and when he saw it was opened, he shouted, "Some fucker has siphoned out our petrol man, it was fucking full man." He walked over to ET and asked him if he had seen anyone stealing his petrol. ET swallowed hard now realising where Ram Jam got the petrol. "No, I just arrived here" he replied.

The group tried unsuccessfully to get into Ram Jam's Taxi. After being denied, they got out and turned back to ET saying, "He won't take the five of us."

Having just witnessed how volatile Ram Jam could be, ET said, "We can only legally take four." Therefore, one guy walked back and got into Ram Jam's car while the two couples chose ET's car.

The two taxis were heading together over the Rathmines Bridge, when, suddenly, Kieran noticed some object being chucked out of Ram Jams driver's window.

Kieran's passengers were too busy pulling the tits and pussy's out of the girls to notice.

As another object was thrown, and then another, Kieran turned off for Mount Pleasant Avenue and dropped off the guys outside their flat. Ram Jam, on the other hand, was supposedly going to Rathgar with the other guy.

As ET passed Rathmines Garda Station, he noticed Ram Jam's Taxi; so, he stopped and walked over, just as two large Cops were dragging the black guy from the back of Ram Jam's Taxi, shouting, "You dirty bastard."

As soon as the Cops disappeared into the station, Kieran asked Ram Jam what happened, and what was he throwing out the window. Ram Jam, even higher than usual answered, in his thicker Jamaican accent, "I'd be turning up the heater and watching my new friend falling asleep."

The heater trick was a familiar tool used by some un-scrupulous Taxi Drivers, after a night on the drink to-gether with tiredness; all you had to do was to ramp up the heater and your passenger would fall into a state of unconsciousness in minutes. Most did it to extend the fare but, sadly, some would take advantage of the situation to molest or even rape their sleeping female passengers.

Meanwhile, Ram Jam continued still in character, "As soon as he was asleep, I reached into his pocket and snatched his wallet, taking me his cash, I fucked out the wallet, then I took his shoes and fucked them out, then I zipped his jeans down and pulled down his jocks. I'd be taking me a sachet of mayonnaise and squirted it over his bongos and on his hand, I went straight into the Garda Station and told the police that a Blackman was mastur-bating in the back of my Taxi, they were very helpful, they're charging him with non-payment of a taxi fare and exposing himself."

After that, Ram Jam started to dance hands up in the air, singing the lyrics of a Bob Marley song, "No woman, no cry, no woman, no cry, everything is going to be al-right, everything is going to be alright."

Driver 69, "Gorgeous George"

It was Friday night, one of the busiest nights back then, John on the Base called.

"Driver 69, I have one of your sisters on here looking for you." A sister was a code for a fuck thing. "She's in Donnybrook." which gave George her location.

George pimped himself out to the married and older women, emotionally extorting money for his services. He would tell them that he was renting the Taxi and couldn't afford to take time off, so many offered to pay his night's earnings for his time.

When asked straight out if he would fuck for money, George would charge fifty pound and if they were ugly or really old, being 40 was a pensioner to him, he would charge them double. His favourite pastime was dipping their handbags as they sucked him-off, often parking under the Base window so John could view the action or holding his microphone open, so John could hear every sound.

His ultimate kink was helping a drunken unconscious husband into his house from his taxi, chatting up his missus and fucking her, preferably next to her husband. This particular sister from Donnybrook was one such obliging wife, who George fondly named "Go, Go."

A week earlier, her husband flagged George's Taxi down in Lesson Street wanting to go home.

As he got into the backseat, he slammed the door hard, but it didn't close. George told him to slam it again, the door didn't close.

George got out and walked around to see what the problem was and discovered that his passenger's leg was still on the road, now bleeding. George grabbed his leg, placed it into his car, and closed the door, laughing his head off as he relayed what just happened to John.

The first rule of a Taxi Driver is: *when carrying a drunk, always make sure to get their address before they nod off.*

The journey to Donnybrook should have been no more than a five-minute drive, but that night, it took over an hour as George took his passenger on a tour of Dublin, stopping off for a kebab as he slept.

Once outside his house George woke him up with the Taxi Drivers' trick for waking up drunks, by grabbing a clump of hair along the neckline and rip it hard.

As usual, the trick worked its magic and his passenger jumped to consciousness, "That's twelve pounds forty-five pence," George told him.

"For fuck's sake! where the fucking hell did you bring me?" the drunk asked. George told him about his imaginary girlfriend that he met in Lesson Street and that he insisted on dropping her off in Tallaght.

Of course, he hadn't a clue who George was talking about, and opening his wallet he fucked two ten-pound notes at George, calling him a "Fucking scum bag" under his breath.

However, as he tried to get out, his leg went from under him, so he screamed in pain, "What fucking happened to my leg?" Slumped on the ground, George offered to help him. He carried his passenger to his front door and pressed the bell.

After three more tries his wife appeared in a black silk robe. She looked at George first and apologised for her husband's condition, asking if he could bring him into the front room.

Always obliging, George did as he was told, while her eyes continued to follow all his movements.

As he entered the living room, she could see how attractive George was, his muscles flexed as he lay her husband down onto the sofa.

"He will be out for the night," she said. Captivated by George's looks, she let slip from her mouth, "God, you're like a model, why are you driving a taxi?" George simply smiled; *Necessity rather than choice* was his mantra. "Did you get paid?" she asked him.

George replied, "The fare was twelve pounds."

The answer shocked the woman, so George repeated the same story he told her husband a couple of minutes earlier, about his female friend going to Tallaght.

"Fucking bastard!" she screamed and upset, she went over to the press, took out her purse, took out twenty pounds, and while giving it to George she said, "Here, you have been so kind."

George smiled and took the money.

With forty pounds in his pocket, he decided it was time to unleash his charm. "I don't know why he bothers, when he has such a beautiful wife like you."

She was physically flattered, again fixing her hair she replied, "You are so kind."

George looked at her and kept going, "You are truly stunning."

Then, she looked at him embarrassed, "Would you like a cup of tea?" she offered, which of course he accepted, while she tightened her robe so he could see her firm tits and erect nipples.

George who was a master in the art of seduction, humbly asked, "It's very warm in here would you mind if I took off my jumper?"

"Of course," she replied.

As he removed his jumper, he deliberately lifted his T-shirt, revealing his six-pack, all the while observing her eyes, which were now focused on his abdomen, "My, you really are like Adonis," she whispered.

She let her robe fall lose revealing her ample breasts for him to see, he bent over and kissed her softly and slowly, with the tips of his fingers stroking her neck as his tongue explored her mouth, his hands travelled down across her breasts, gently caressing the silk over them, she let out a soft sigh, neither of them said a word as softly lay her on the floor and opened her robe, "God you're beautiful," he repeated over and over, continuing to passionately kiss her.

As his lips covered her breasts, his fingers circled her wet pussy teasing her inner thighs, she moaned harder. In the meantime, George kept looking at her husband on the sofa, asleep; his lips were now kissing her pussy, his hands squeezing and fondling her breasts, teasing her erect nipples. Then, while his tongue was exploring her deep and his fingers were rhythmically caressing her g-spot, she orgasmed into his mouth and he consumed her cum like a vacuum, smiling.

Slowly, he lifted his face from her pussy and kissed every part of her body back to her lips; removing his T-shirt, he stood up over her and took off his jeans that re-vealed his huge cock, getting harder as he looked at her unconscious husband.

"Oh my God, that's some cock," she gasped.

He smiled and returned to her lips kissing her as his cock found her soft and very wet pussy, she moaned loudly as he penetrated her, the force of his cock pushed her pussy wide; she came again, he moved down and consumed her cum, turning her over he mounted her ass, fulfilling his desire with a full view of her husband as he fucked his wife doggy style, her tits bobbing back and forth. Her third orgasm was different, just as she climaxed, she screamed loudly "Go, Go, Go!"

Her body tightened as he pumped her harder, her body shuddering as she released a long sigh, collapsing onto her back exhausted, he opened her legs, the veins of his cock bulging, penetrating her again she screamed as he ripped her again, "Oh my God," she screamed as he exploded inside her. "My God, I have never had two orgasms in my life, never mind three. I didn't think that was possible, that's the best sex I have ever had."

George smiled.

"You are a God, by the way, what's your name?" she laughed.

"I'm George, and you?" George kissed her again.

"I'm Angela," she replied.

"That was incredible, truly incredible," Angela uttered, as George stood over her, cum dripping from his cock he placed his fingers to catch it, walked over to Angela's unconscious husband and rubbed it onto his lips, and whispered to him "Who's the scumbag now bitch?"

George turned back smiling and said to her, "Our secret," she laughed.

"You are mad, absolutely mad, am I going to see you again?" she asked as he got dressed.

He gave her the Base's number. "Call me the next time he goes out, I will bring him home for you," they both laughed.

Driver 80, "Nuts"

Alan known as "Nuts" would, without doubt, have a very long medical definition attached to him today, considering that he, more than likely, suffered from sociopathic disorders, or was on the spectrum of autism.

Nevertheless, back in the eighties he was just considered to be "Nuts."

At the end of the seventies, Dublin Corporation as it was known back then, substituted anyone with a provisional licence for a full driving license, and that's how Nuts obtained his driving license.

His brother, who was a year older than him, took the Taxi Test impersonating him. That was possible because most of the official documentation had no picture identification, and the Taxi Test was limited to only three questions. One, would have been "How would you get from Heuston Station to O' Connell Street?" or something similar, while the other two questions would have been about the fare card.

Alan had been in most Taxi companies in Dublin, usually forced to leave over his behaviour. He absolutely had no filter and said the first thing that came into his mind. He couldn't feel empathy, his physical appearance was that of a boy, and he was extraordinarily childlike but at the same time, extremely gifted at impersonating accents and imitating anyone's actions. Today, his condition would be called Echopraxia.

Voluntarily or forced, he left Pony Taxis for allegedly, as there was no evidence or witnesses to him chaining the back axle of a car to a metal railing, causing the railings to be ripped from its pillars, something he had seen on a television programme and thought it was funny.

He joined Kilmore Taxis in early May of nineteen eighty-five and immediately fitted in, with his uncanny sense of humour, practical jokes, and pranks.

No day was ever the same with Nuts, his first day he parked on the Mater Hospital Taxi Rank behind Driver 12, Jumping Johnny, sat in the back seat of his car with two other Taxi Drivers and within minutes he had them mesmerised by his impersonations of Bill Clinton, James Cagney, and Clint Eastwood.

At every Taxi rank he went to, all the drivers wanted to hear him impersonate Hollywood's greats or other drivers, which drove the Base controllers mad.

The CB radios were quite primitive back then, they had two channels, one where you could hear everyone and the other where the driver could only hear the Base controller.

The Base controller, on the other hand, only knew who was calling him by their driver's number.

Nuts usually would pick a driver who was sitting in front of his car and imitate him.

With Buckets in the first car and Nuts in the second, Nuts decided to show off in front of the two other drivers who were sitting in the back of his Taxi while waiting for a fare. As for Buckets, he didn't like newbies as he referred to them, so he usually sat on his own, unless some of the older drivers arrived.

One day, Nuts picked up his mic and called the Base in a flawless imitation of Bucket's accent, "Driver 22 I'm engaged to Wicklow."

Arthur, on the Base replied, "Wow, it must be your lucky day Driver 22, is away to Wicklow."

They could see Buckets picking up his mic, switching channel, they heard him calling the Base, "Driver 22 I'm not going to Wicklow, I'm still on the rank" Arthur called back "Okay, you are still parked, have you parked first."

Nuts keyed his mic again imitating Bucket's and said, "Driver 22 I'm engaged to Wicklow."

Arthur replied, "Okay Driver 22 you are away to Wicklow again."

Buckets picked up his mic and called Arthur, "No I'm not, now stop acting the bollox."

The drivers in Nuts Taxi were pissing themselves, Arthur went quiet, so Nuts called in again as Buckets and screamed, "Are you fucking smoking dope you thick cunt?"

Arthur replied, "There is no need for that language Driver 22, and no, I don't do drugs."

To that, the real Buckets respond, "What are you fucking talking about? I don't give a fuck if you're on drugs and I don't fucking use bad language."

Nuts never knowing when to stop, called in again, "Driver 22 away to Wicklow," so Arthur asked again, "Driver 22 are you away to Wicklow?"

Buckets picked up his mic and shouted, "If I go up to that Base, I will kick you to fucking Wicklow and back, now fuckoff about Wicklow!"

Arthur didn't reply.

Driver 6, poor Peter, having just joined the Taxi rank, got out of his taxi and was about to get into Nuts'.

Nuts opened his door and said, "Would you ask yer man in front of me if he is going to Wicklow?"

Peter, as instructed, tapped on Buckets window, and asked him if he was going to Wicklow.

Buckets jumped out of his car, grabbed Peter by the throat leaving poor Peter's legs dangling in the air, Buckets smashed him onto the bonnet of his car, shouting at him "I'll fucking Wicklow you."

Everyone was in stitches and kept laughing as they tried to pull Buckets off Peter, Nuts standing in the middle of them impersonating a referee from the WWF saying, "In the red car we have Buckets of Blood, weighing in at two hundred and twenty pounds, sixteen ko's and in the white car we have."

Then, Nuts imitated a TV ad about penguin bars adapting it to the situation, "Pick up, a Peter, weighing eight ounces, nineteen bouts of diarrhoea, no wins, loads of submissions," even ending his commentary with "that, that, that's all folks."

Peter now shaking, got into Nuts car along with the other drivers. "What's his problem?" Peter asked.

In a perfect Jimmy Stewart accent, Nuts replied, "He suffers from Wicklowphobia, one mention of it, drives him insane;" then adopting Jack Nicholson's facial expressions from The Shinning repeated the words "Here's Johnny."

Peter just looked at him in amazement.

Nuts had many peculiarities, from whistling or screaming at cyclists as they turned a corner, with the intention of making them fall, to using his super soaker out his window late at night, soaking revellers.

By far, his favourite pastime was pranking his passengers, sitting on the Gresham taxi rank in Dublin's O' Connell Street across from Rumours Night Club.

Two Ballymun afro's as they were fondly termed by the Taxi Drivers, quick definition, Lipstick scaffolding, eyeliner, plastered make-up, boobtube, teeny-winy skirt, and bottle bleached blonde hair, wearing the signature six inch white high heels, carrying the big black leather handbag that smuggled their bottle of vodka, some, not all of them wore knickers, trying to get into the back seat of a car while wrapped in tight material that was no bigger than a belt, never left anything to the imagination, usually they were that pissed they just hiked up their skirts revealing everything, putting one leg into the Taxi and falling into the back seat after it.

The two, that were just about to get into Nuts car, were late thirties with spare tyres laced with cellulite hanging over their miniskirts, most coming from a nightclub usually spoke loudly when they came out because of the loud music. These two obviously thought they were speaking normally; when, in fact they were shouting.

In their very distinctive Dublin Moore Street accent, one said to the other "Let's wind up the Taxi Man," "I'll pretend to puke," the other replied.

But Nuts had his window down and heard every word; they got into his back seat, one revealing her bare ass to all the Taxi Drivers that were waiting for the show.

Nuts turned around to catch the front, a large growth of black pubic hair between her legs.

Nuts asked with a profound stammer "Where, where, where are you, you off toooo?" startled, one replied, "Yeah love, we're off to Ballymun in the sun."

Nuts brought his left hand to his shoulder, bending his body. Grabbling the gear lever in a jerking motion with an open hand, then sitting back straight, bending back over to close each finger around the gear stick.

"Ahh Jesus, he's one of these fucking handicapped Taxi fellas," the girl behind Nuts said to her friend.

"Fuckoff he shouldn't be driving a fucking Taxi, sure he can't touch the fucking gear thingy Betty," her friend said.

In his perfect Christy Browne impersonation, Nuts interrupted them and said, "I'm not, not, handi, handi caped, I'm dis, dis, dis, abled and, and I, I can drive as, as good as, as the next man." Nuts went to change gear again, doing the whole bending simulation thing deliberately leaving his head under the windscreen a bit longer so the car veered off, the girls screamed, "Fucking Jesus keep your head up."

Betty turned around sobering up quick and said, "Mags, he's going to get us fucking killed."

Nuts interrupted them, "Do do do any of you know how how to drive?" "Why?"

Mags answered, "So you you can pull pull my gear thingy." Mags looked at Betty and gestured with her thumb to get out of the car.

Nuts was just turning onto the Ballymun road which has four lanes, there wasn't a car insight, so he started to imitate Jumping Johnny, his head violently jerking back and forth, the car veering off to the side, the girls screaming in the back, "Jesus for fuck sake what's happening to him?"

Betty replied, "He's having one of those fits grab the wheel Mags."

Nuts resumed to normal mode and said in Tattoo's voice from Fantasy Island "Thank you for flying with Kilmore Taxis, I hope the journey was entertaining."

Betty was first to smack Nuts in the back of the head, "You fucking bastard, I thought I was going to fucking die;"

Nuts replied, "And I thought you were going to wind wind wind me up."

"You're a fucking bastard, I'm going to report you," Mags told him.

They paid him the fare and as they were getting out Nuts asked them if they could give him a hand getting reverse. They both said, "You fucking prick."

Coincidentally, some weeks later, one of them got into Jumping Johnny's car and when he had a spasm, she slapped him across the head and told him to "Fuckoff with the bouncing."

Poor Peter and the Bal-e-er Boot boy

Poor Peter's next memorable incident was created this time by his passenger, sitting in the back of his Cab, a nutjob off his head on glue, from Ballyfermot better known as Bal-e-er, the man had his face pressed against the glass while making distorted faces at drivers in cars which were passing by.

One driver in a Fiat 850 pulled up beside Peter and winding down his window shouted with a bad speech impediment "Are you fucking slagging me?"

Peter looked to his right and noticed the man; he too put his window down and received a hail of abuse.

Peter, for some reason decided it was the right time to use the advice he received from Buckets of Blood, on how to never back down and always attack. Buckets called it "Taxi survival for dummies." So, adopting his new skills, Peter replied in his sudo, but still refined accent, "Why don't you just fuck-off?"

At that moment, the driver of the Fiat slammed on his brakes, swung his driver's door open, and then disappeared for a moment, only to reappear with crutches supporting his tiny frame.

The wannabe boot boy from Bal-e-er was in hysterics, laughing at the little guy waving his crutches like a Dalek from *Doctor Who*. By this time, he had his head out the window shouting, "Did you fall out of your pram?"

Sadly, the driver of the Fiat thought Peter said it, and for that, he wacked Peter across the face with the heavy crutch.

The Bal-e-e-r boot boy still hanging out the window, shouted again, "Look at the balls on the Dwarf!" leading

35

the driver of the Fiat to smack Peter's back window in retaliation, missing it and hitting the glass instead.

Now covered in glass, Peter was on his radio calling for help, and just by chance, it was John who answered the call, who was on the Base that day; and this is how this story played out across the taxi Airwaves of Dublin.

"Lads, Driver 6 is having a Charlie on Rathmines Road, a midget, sorry physically challenged man is smacking Peter's car with his crutches. No, I didn't say crotch, I said crutch. Anyway, is there anyone around that can give Peter a hand?"

A volley of comments replied, "Maybe Babs will give him a hand, did he not find Miss Cum-in-a-flood?"

"If he's a midget, he would only have little hands," another driver called in after only hearing half of the story.

The traffic was backed up to the bridge because of Peter's car and the Fiat blocking the road.

Driver 44, known as The Friesion, because of his huge cow-like head and his Cork accent, the thickest, which most couldn't decipher.

Every second word he used was "Fucking" but because of his accent it sounded like "Bucking."

The Friesion was on the scene to report back to John, who, in turn, eloquently re-laid to everyone "There's a bucking little bucking fella with bucking sticks in a little bucking suit spitting at poor bucking Peter."

Things started to escalate when the Bal-e-er boot boy picked up the Fiat driver and started to swing him, singing "Round and round the garden like a teddy bear."

Crutches went flying hitting some bystander who started a fight with the Friesion, who at the time, was trying to assist poor Peter and his black eye, the result of the first crutch attack.

Trapped between the two cars, the bystander was facing off the Friesion, who attacked the bystander locking his teeth onto his nose; blood went everywhere, the Fiat driver all the while screaming "Let me go!" which the Bal-e-er boot boy did, mid-flight launching the Fiat driver into an oncoming car. Peter screamed at the Bal-e-er boot boy, "What did you do that for?"

The Bal-e-er boot boy replied in his half brain dead accent, "Did he not ask me to let him go?"

The driver of the oncoming car was howling at the Fiat driver who had landed on the front of his car shouting, "Look at the dent you caused!"

The Bal-e-er boot boy, stopped the oncoming car driver by saying, "It's only a little dent, sure he's a little fucker, are you insured for flying midgets, you didn't try to avoid him, you hit him, I've seen it, I could be a witness," which set the oncoming car driver off. "He was fucking in the air, how could I possibly, fucking avoid, a flying fucking midget?"

The Bal-e-er boot boy replied, "Now, now, man, he's not a midget, he is physically stunted."

The oncoming car driver shouted back, "What the fuck was he doing in the fucking air?"

The Fiat driver interrupted the two of them and replied, "I was going for fucking dancing lessons, what do you fucking think, this moron pointing at the Bal-e-er boot boy was assaulting me, poor Peter was slumped over crying in the front seat of his Taxi."

By the time the Police arrived the Friesion had left the scene leaving the bystander unconscious.

Warning poor Peter not to open his mouth, the Bal-e-er boot boy fucked off with poor Peter's jacket and wallet, the oncoming car driver left on foot because he had no insurance, and the Fiat driver before leaving took his crutch and smashed Poor Peter's front window.

Poor Peter tried, as best as he could, to explain to the Cops how a glue sniffing maniac picked up a midget, swung him into oncoming traffic, and how the midget went berserk and smashed his taxi.

The two Cops, amused by the story, trying to hold the laughter asked Peter, "What happened to your man stretched out there on the ground?"

Peter replied, "I didn't notice him," the Cop looking at the oncoming car driver's car with a big dent in the bonnet, turned to Peter and said, "Ahh, sure this is a civil matter, move your car and be on with, yeah."

Two nights later, Poor Peter called in Driver 6, have two new windows and was ready for work.

As faith would have it, John was working the Base again, and he asked Peter, if he was around Donnycarney.

Every driver knew the time and place to avoid "Stink Bag," an obese thirty stone argumentative schizo that suffered from incontinence.

John asked Peter if he had a magic tree in his car. Peter replied in his distinctive accent, that his car was brand new, and he had just valeted it. "Do you have electric windows?" John asked, and Peter, gave him a list of all the extras his new Peugeot 405 had, including beige velour upholstery, John emphasising it all continued, "That's lovely, beige velour upholstery, do you have seat covers?" John inquired.

The following is the narration John gave, including the communication over-heard between Poor Peter and John.

"Sorry Driver 6, I don't have anyone else, is there a problem?" John asked.

"This giant is stuck in my door, and he has a distinct odour of urine," Peter answered.

John rephrased, and replied over the air, "You have a man stuck and he is banging of piss, where is he stuck?"

Peter replied, "He's wedged between my back door, holding back the laughter." John started to give Peter instructions on how to unwedge him.

"Peter, get your shoulder and give him a shove, sure he will pop in, do you have any gel or lube to put along the door?"

Peter now furious, replied, "What the hell would I be doing with gel or lube?"

Quick-witted, John replied, "Some of the drivers use lube on their clutch cables, or gel for the hair," John continued with his instructions, "get him to shimmy back and forth," knowing well Peter wouldn't know what to shimmy meant.

On queue, Peter asked, "It's like when you're riding," massive pause.

"Have you ever ridden a horse, Peter?" John asked. His unmistakable laughter, set the entire taxi fleet into hysterics, "Get him to ride the door. Your hole is lifting, sorry your whole car is lifting, Jesus that would have been painful," eventually Peter got him into the back of his car and closed the door.

John recapped for all, "That's great! You got him in after a bit of riding, and you didn't need lube or gel, fair play to yeah Peter, did you wash your hands, Peter?"

"Driver 6 is off to the RDS to see Elton John. Very good Peter, call me when you are free. Sorry Lads, quite please, Driver 6, go ahead, Lads Driver 6 is having a Charlie."

Peter replied that his passenger's incontinent bag had burst due to the door riding and his car was covered in excrement.

John's reply was genius, "Your car is covered in mint, was he eating chocolate, what's x-mints Peter, oh shite, your car is covered in shite, he had a bag full of shite with him. What was he doing with a bag full of shite? Peter, how does he go to the toilet in a bag? Jesus the mind boggles, he is blaming you, how is he blaming you? did you burst his bag of shite? Oh, he's claiming he burst it when he was riding your door."

Driver 12, known as Jumping Johnny because of his involuntary spasm that made his head violently jerk back and forth, was first to arrive and found Peter sitting crying, the back of his new car covered in liquid shite, his obese passenger standing with his trousers covered in shite too.

Johnny, in the attempt to console Peter said, "Ah, sure it could be worse.. you could have got him on a Thursday, he fucking devours those curries, God the whiff!"

Peter was looking up at Johnny when, suddenly, a spasm sent Johnny's head back and forth.

Peter screamed, "What the fuck, what's happening to you?" Peter grabbed his mic and called in saying that Johnny was having a fit and his head was spinning like the exorcist.

Once again, John's twisted sense of humour, which had no boundaries, was released, "Was it the smell of shite that made him fit? that happens to me when I smell sick. How far back is his head going?"

Peter, now in a state of shock trying to help, called out, "Are you all right?" as quickly as the spasm came, it was gone.

Johnny replied, "What are you talking about?"

Deliberately winding Peter up, he said "Of course I'm all right, why wouldn't I be?"

Peter, even more confused, tried to explain what had just happened, something that Johnny denied by saying that he must have been hallucinating because of some Moroccan Black he smoked.

Peter replied that he didn't smoke and had no idea about what the hell was Moroccan.

It took five days for Peter to get a new back seat and a new floor carpet; sadly, he couldn't match the colour and now he found himself with a beige velour in the front and a brown in the back, something which gave John endless amusement, so much so that during Peter's first night back, John asked him, "Did the shite dye the upholstery brown?"

A fad swept Dublin in the early nineties where teenagers put Loctite super glue on seats, handrails, doors, or any surface someone might put their hand on.

Peter was sitting on College Green taxi rank and needed to go to the toilet; so, he told Arthur, the Base controller.

Thirty minutes later the Base got a call from the pub where Peter had gone to the toilet, informing him that Peter had sat on a toilet seat and his ass was now glued to it. The fire brigade was cutting the seat off, Arthur informed the fleet, and everyone showed up just as Peter was being carried out with his trousers around his ankles and a black toilet seat stuck to his ass.

Of course, sympathy was the last thing he got from John when Peter returned three days later.

"Welcome back Peter, I was told you had a delicate issue, yes that's terrible. Did you not give the aul seat the rub before you sat down? How did they remove it? Stressing it from your ass? Do you have like a tattoo of a toilet seat on your ass now, what does your missus think of it?"

Then, John went on to tell every driver who didn't already hear about Peter's ass being Loctite, to a toilet seat.

For months afterwards, when Peter was sitting on a Taxi rank for more than ten minutes John would say, "Jesus, you must be glued to that seat."

Peter got more than his share of pukers, pissers, masturbators, and runners because of his serious lack of street smarts, however, his most memorable ones were, of course, on the nights John was on the Base.

Peter and the "Traveller King"

Poor Peter never seemed to learn from his mistakes, or the warnings from others. On more than one occasion, Buckets tried to school him "what to do, and not to do" when driving a taxi, mainly because he viewed Peter as an easy touch to score money from, selling him illegal weapons that he called personal protection equipment that he doubled in price, to doggy tins of foam to fill his tyres when Peter got a puncture.

Coming from a very sheltered white-collar upbringing, Peter considered Buckets to be one of Dublin's mafias and, although Peter was shit scared of Buckets, he felt he needed him to survive in a world he called "The Zoo."

The Camelot Hotel was located in Coolock, on Dublin's Northside, notorious for the Travelling Community, or as they were referred to back in the Eighties as "Knackers." It was a *no-go area* for everyone other than their own.

The Camelot was a nightclub like no other as at least two stolen cars would be burnt out each night, an occurrence they affectionately called a *Barbeque*.

In the grounds of its car park most nights, people could find themselves in the middle of stabbings and waging feuds between the different travelling communities; the security guards who guarded the doors, coming all from the inner city, Dublin's hardest and most violent place.

Peter was returning from dropping a fare in Artane when he got a flag down from a young girl just down from the Camelot Hotel, dressed in a mini skirt, boob tube, knee length leatherette red boots, and caked in makeup. She got into the back of his car and said in a very distinctive travellers' accent, "I'm go-n to a Lab-Ray Park in Bally-fer- mot."

Peter asked her to repeat what she said, "I'm go-n to Lab-Ray Park in Bally-fer- mot, are yee deaf?"

Peter apologised and called John, "Driver 6, just picked up and away to," in his posh accent. Peter pronounced it "Labray Park, in Ballyfermot."

John knowing all too well that Labre Park was a Travellers halting site, was trying to warn Peter, "You might meet Charlie there, Peter."

Peter replied, "No, I don't think so, very quiet, a sweet little girl."

John replied, "Do you know that area Peter?" which led Peter to Tell John, "That he once done the accounts for a company in Bluebell."

John replied, "God Peter, you really get around."

Peter tried to make conversation with the girl asking her if she had a good night.

"I'd not be fucking yee, yey got it," she replied.

Peter shocked replied, "I'm not interested in that type of thing," which fired up the traveller, "Yey saying I'm fuckn ugly or what?"

Peter didn't reply, and while passing over Ballybough bridge she shouted, "fuckn Bastard is coming out of me fanny."

Peter turned around, she had her hand between her legs, he snapped back his head, looking forward.

She said, "Did yee get an eye full, yee fuckn pervert?"

Peter replied by saying he thought she was in trouble, which lit a match inside her, she screamed at Peter, "You think be-cus me be-n a knacker I'm in trouble, hav-n a ba-bee out euf wedlock, I'm some Ges- a- bell, I'm a day-cent woman, I wood-ent be riding the likes of yee."

Peter started to drive quicker, she smacked Peter across the face, screaming at him, "Did yee hear me?"

Peter replied, "Look, I'm sorry, you misunderstood what I said."

She replied, "Are yee calln me stu-pid of some-what?"

Peter replied, "Not at all, we are just here," and as he turned into the travelling site, the penny dropped in Peter's mind what John was trying to tell him.

She opened the door and was getting out when Peter shouted, "Miss, you have to pay the fare."

She ignored him and opened the door of a caravan, stepped in, and closed it.

The fare was twelve pounds, quite a lot of money back then. Peter blew into John, telling him what happened.

John replied, "Could have been worse, put it down to experience."

But Buckets had drilled into Peter's head to never let anyone away with a fare; you have to stand your ground.

As a result, Peter got out his Chinese Police baton he bought from Buckets and concealed in his hand, he knocked on the door. Nobody answered, he knocked again, saying "Young lady, you have to pay the fare."

The caravan door swung open; Peter looked up at a giant of a man wearing nothing other than his white under pants. "What yee be wan-tin?" he asked Peter.

Peter replied, "I just dropped off a young girl, she went into your mobile home."

He replied, "There bee no yung- n in me van, now fuckoff." He slammed the caravan door shut.

45

Peter was in a state of shock, and trying to get away fast, he accidentally tripped over a brush that hit the caravan; a fact which angered the giant knacker, who came out, picked Peter up by his throat and said, "Do yee wan me to bee cut-n yer balls off? I kick thee head of yea."

Without thinking, Peter raised his right hand and pressed the button on the Chinese police baton, which resulted in a hundred pounds of pressure to be released as the inch steel pole landed right in the middle of the giant's forehead.

Still holding Peter by the throat, the giant kept looking at Peter with a big smile on his face, as if time was running in slow motion. Peter swallowed hard, knowing his life was about to end violently, but, lucky for him, the giant knacker started to sway, his hand let go of Peter's throat, and then, like a tree, he fell slowly and keeled over, hitting the corner of a steel oil drum on his way down.

Peter, froze, still holding the Police Baton and whispered to himself, "What have I done.?"

He slowly approached the giant's figure but when a light went on in another caravan, Peter quickly jumped into his car and while taking off, he immediately called John, "Driver 6, I think I might have killed somebody."

John replied, "Say that again, Driver 6?"

Peter told him the story of what happened.

John organised for Driver 69 to reach him, Gorgeous George, who was dropping a fare in Walkinstown to collect the stinger bar, as John called it.

George went straight to Peter, took the Police Baton, and instructed Peter to go to a phone box and phone the Base. He told Peter exactly what to say to the police, that the giant grabbed him and subsequentially lost his balance and fell. That he, Peter, was scared for his life, and that he had left the site because he thought the others would have killed him, and because he thought the giant was okay.

An hour later, John called Peter, "Driver 6, have the Garda from Ballyfermot on here, did you have an incident earlier in Ballyfermot?" So, Peter knew the giant was not dead.

John said, "A gentleman is claiming you hit him," the laughs of the other drivers filled the airwaves. John had to chastise them like children. "Come on lads, the guards are listening here."

John asked Peter if he could drop over to the Garda station in Ballyfermot.

Peter said, "No problem," and as soon as the guards were off the phone, John told Peter to call him.

John told Peter the knacker was okay, who, almost collapsed from relief in the phone box.

John advised him to go over and say exactly what he just said over the air, informing him that the guard heard everything.

Peter asked John how the police got his car number, and apparently, it was from someone who took his number while he was leaving.

Fifty minutes later, Peter walked into Ballyfermot Garda station on Drumfin Road. He went to the counter and told the Garda that he was the driver involved in the incident at Labre Park, where the giant fell.

A detective appeared and asked Peter for the keys to his car and to follow him into a room where the giant was sitting.

On seeing the giant, Peter's face drained of all its colour. The giant had, what looked like half a tennis ball growing out of his forehead, where the baton hit him.

Suddenly, the giant stood up, Peter was eye level to his chest, and in that moment the Cop said to the giant, "Mr Cash, is this the man that knocked you out?"

The giant looked down at Peter and laughing he answered, "That fuckn leprechaun couldn't knock the King of the Travellers out."

Raising his large hands, surprisingly kept saying "the guy that hit me was so tall," pointing nearly another foot over Peter's head.

As a consequence, the detective dismissed the case by saying, "Sorry about that mix up" to Peter, and then beckoning him to get out of the room.

As soon as Peter was outside, the detective turned to him and said, "You're a lucky man, he would never admit that a little fella like you could have done so much damage to him, his reputation would be destroyed."

To that, Peter replied, "I didn't touch him, he fell over."

Another detective drew near and handed Peter his keys, shaking his head to his colleague.

John had warned Peter the Cops would search his car, the detective told Peter, "I've been doing this job for almost twenty years, and I can tell you," looking deep into Peter's face, "what hit that knacker, was a Chinese Police baton. Now, I'm not saying you did, but someone did, my advice to you is, don't be working over this side of the city for a long while."

In the end, Peter never collected the Chinese police baton from George and didn't accept a job anywhere on the southside that would take him near the Travellers' camp.

Driver 22, "Shirley"

Known as Shirley Temple, Vincent was thirty-eight and a closet homosexual from Limerick. Rumour had it, he was a former priest, back in the eighties (queer bashing was rampant) in Dublin, being gay was very dangerous to your well-being. Regardless, Vincent could be found parked outside Ireland's only Gay Club waiting for a fare or an affair, as he used to say.

His sense of humour was lost on John, the Base controller. John was homophobic, so he always felt uncomfortable responding to Shirley, and for that he was mostly abrupt or nasty towards him. John enjoyed sending him to biker's clubs or brothels to collect clients.

No night went by without some rude comment by John, like, if Shirley arrived on a taxi rank and announced that he was parked behind, John would reply, "Bet you like that position" or "Shirley is behind Driver 70, watch your ass;" "I bet you, he would make your hole weak, Driver 70," or "I bet sex with him would be a pain in the ass." However, John's favourite one was, "Shirley is wanked on Coolock, sorry ranked on Coolock."

Despite the malevolent teasing, Vincent let the comments wash off, always ready with a witty response, his favourites being, "I'm blowing you John, and you're not responding," "don't knock it until you try it" - a love hate relationship that lasted between them for years.

One night between a Saturday and a Sunday, Shirley had just dropped a fare in Harold's Cross at four am, he was driving down Leinster Road and towards Rathmines.

As he passed the old Georgian redbrick houses, now converted into flats, a guy, wearing nothing else but a plastic moss peat bag, appeared out of the bushes. He raised his arm to flag Shirley down, and in so doing, he let the bag drop revealing his manhood for Shirley to view. Immediately, Shirley stopped and leaned over to open his front passenger door for the guy to get in.

He was completely covered in cuts, and in his very deep Dublin accent said, "Quick man, fucking drive."

Shirley knew he wasn't going to be lucky with this one. "I'm a Taxi man's son, I'm going to Finglas. Cheers for stopping man it was fucking mad."

Now, the worst question a Taxi Driver can ask his passenger is, "Are you okay?" which normally follows with their life story; but in this case, Shirley was dying to find out what happened, so he asked.

"Man, I scored this hottie in Bad Bobs, little mini skirt, big bouncy tits, you know what I mean. God, she was fucking gorgeous…said she was a nurse, invites me back to hers, squeezing me cock and balls out of me in the Taxi back to Rathmines, gets to her flat, goes in, and we get busy on the sofa, she strips me, I'm bollick naked and gagging for it, big hard on. She says, she needs to go to the bog, and all of a sudden, two big fuckers walk in, thump the head off me. I'm lying in a heap, then this mad thing comes in, she was like a witch, about ninety, wearing all black with a fucking stick the size of herself and starts whacking me across the back and right up between my legs in the balls, calling me a dirty bastard. Screaming, I needed to be saved. Yer one I was with appears wearing all black too, she has a fucking pot of water and, she's fucking throwing it over me, the two giants are holding my legs and arms, the witch grabs me balls and starts yanking me nutsack, chanting, these are the demons, I will remove them. Jesus, man, the other one, is slapping me with the fucking stick across me back like a mad thing. I thought they were going to chop off me, bollocks. I pissed myself, piss went everywhere, the lads let me go, yer one throws the water over me, and the witch whacks me a dozen times. I scarpered over to the window, looked out and seen a glass house and jumped through the window, straight through the fucking roof of the glass house, looks around and there is a bag of Moss Peat, empties that and ran and hid in the bushes. He put his hand down the plastic bag and said, fucking Moss Peat is up me hole."

As Shirley pulled up the traffic lights in-Drumcondra, Driver 34, Aka Donuts, pulled up alongside Shirley's taxi and told John, "There is a naked guy in Shirley's car."

John repeated it for all, "Driver 22, have you got a naked guy in your car?"

Shirley responded, "Of course not! No, he's not naked, he's wearing a moss peat bag," to which John responded for all to hear. "Ahh, that's okay, he's not naked, he's wearing a moss peat bag, is that the new fashion, what does he wear on Sunday, a Dunnes Stores bag?"

The airwaves filled with suggestions, if he gets lost, he could wear a milk carton, or if he's feeling sexy, he could wear cling film, maybe if he's a prick, he could wear a condom.

Again, John feigned annoyance as he chastised the drivers for the cruel comments. John responded, "It's okay lads, he's a Taxi Drivers Son," which started them off again.

Peter goes looking for a Prostitute

Poor Peter's first passenger looking for a prostitute.

It all started when John received a call from Bob, a known Fitzwilliam Square dog looking to pick up a prostitute. Usually, the experienced ones never used their own cars, just in case they got spotted by a colleague, or neighbour, or got stopped by the police, and if they were, they would not hesitate to put the blame on the Taxi Driver over a misunderstanding.

John went about setting Poor Peter up and deliberately gave him a job that would lead him into town and then told him to collect a solicitor on Haddington Road *going local.*

As soon as the other drivers heard where Peter was picking up, the slagging started, "Hope Saint Peter has his rosary beads polished."

"Is that solicitor looking for his Holy places?"

"Ask Shirley if he's holding confession, that's not the only thing Shirley would be holding. He's doing God's work. Gods not a Prostitute."

"No, but he knew a few,"

"Where they from Fitzwilliam?"

"Mary Madelyn."

"Does she work the Pepper Canister?"

Yet, even with all the chatter, Peter still didn't realise that he was being set up.

Bob was mid-forties and appeared impeccably dressed in his Louis Copeland suit and handmade shoes, while stepping into Peter's taxi. Peter thought "he's one of my own," which meant that he didn't have to put on his false persona.

"Where to?" Peter asked.

"Just drive around the Square, I'm looking for someone in particular," he said.

"Sorry, what Square?" Peter asked in his normal accent.

"You mustn't be driving a taxi long," Bob replied, pointing directions that Peter followed.

As Peter drove around Fitzwilliam Square, Bob noticed a young blonde in a bright yellow t-shirt with big tits. "That's her," he shouted, ordering Peter to pull up beside her.

"Is she your daughter?" Peter asked.

Bob just gave him a glance and said, "Are you brain dead?"

Peter replied, "There is no call to be rude."

Bob pressed the window down and called the girl over.

"Are they real?" he asked her.

To that, Peter nearly choked on his polo mint.

"Show me your tits," Bob directed the girl.

She lifted her T-shirt, and her huge tits bounced out.

Peter was trying to come to terms with what was happening, as Bob lunged out Peter's window and locked his hands on her tits. The screams of the prostitute filling the night air.

Peter grabbed his microphone and called in, "Peter, oh I mean Driver 6, I'm having a Charlie, a Charlie, help."

John called out the Charlie and told everyone to be quiet, "Where are you Peter?" John asked.

"I'm on a Square with this man beside me swinging on a lady's breasts."

"Is his name Bob by any chance?" John replied.

Peter, now in a state of shock lost all rational thought, "Yes yes, his name is Bob."

The screams of the young Prostitute pierced John's ears as Bob squeezed her breasts harder.

"Ahh, that's Tits Bob, everyone knows him."

John informed the rest of the fleet to stand down as it was only Tits Bob, "You will have to break his hold," John instructed Peter.

"I will have to do what?" Peter replied.

The young girl kept screaming as she tried to break Bob's hold.

Peter, accidentally held his microphone open; therefore, every driver could hear him say in the poshest accent, "You will have to release that girl this instant."

John, along with the fleet, was bent up laughing.

Peter repeated his demand to Bob, while reciting the rosary.

Then, out of nowhere, a very large man with a baseball bat appeared who promptly smashed the stick over Bob's head.

"Oh, sweet Jesus," Peter screamed.

The drivers started calling in asking if Jesus was on Fitzwilliam Square with Peter.

Others replied, "No, he is with Shirley."

Now unconscious, Bob's hands released the young prostitute.

She pushed her nails into his head and dragged them down his face, screaming "You fucking bastard!"

Bob remained unresponsive to her attack; his body still hanging out Peter's window.

The guy with the bat, not content to have knocked Bob unconscious, he also smashed Bob's shoulder.

Peter's taxi shuddered.

John asked Peter, if he was all right, not realising the girl's pimp was whacking the crap out of Bob.

"John, John" Peter screamed into the mic, "there's a man with a baseball bat whacking Bob."

John responded, "There is a guy wanking Bob, is that what you said Peter? Get the Police, get the Police!" Peter screamed.

John replied, realising Peter was petrified, "Are you okay?"

Peter replied, "Never in my life, have I ever witnessed anyone punch another person, and here I am, in the middle of Dublin city, with a solicitor who was swinging out of some prostitute's breasts, being pulverised by some maniac."

John called out, "Cops are on their way Peter."

The pimp heard John and bent down to look through Peter's passengers window; with his head now resting on Bob's back, he reached into his pockets, took his wallet, and watch, his eyes fixed on Peter's face.

The young girl took the bat from her pimp and tried to hit Bob again, but she missed and hit Peter's front window instead. The glass shattered and covered Peter.

The Pimp looked at Peter and said, "You didn't see fucking anything. Got it?"

Just as they disappeared, the police arrived, coincidence or just bad timing, the Cops were the same two that were called to Peter's incident two weeks earlier in Rathmines.

As the first one got out of the patrol car, he turned to the other and said, "It's Tits Bob, and yer man in the Peugeot with the flying midget."

Peter overhearing him, still with the microphone in his hand asked, "Does everyone in fucking Dublin know this Tits Bob?"

Just as the Cops approached Peter's taxi, Bob started to regain consciousness.

One Cop tended to Bob, and the other opened Peter's door.

Peter got quickly out and hugged the Cop, "I've never been so happy to see a policeman in my life," he said, still holding the cop.

"What happened here, sir?" the Cop kept asking Peter.

Buckets of Blood, together with Ram Jam, arrived at the same time and went over to Peter, telling the Cop to let Peter go, thinking the Cop was roughing up Peter for a statement.

Peter had just turned when Buckets grabbed him away from the Cop, whispering in Peter's ear, "Don't say a word, these fuckers will kill you and your family."

Needless to say, Buckets and the pimp were friends.

Bob, now conscious, and realising how serious the situation was, said, "Guards, there has been a terrible misunderstanding, I'm not pressing charges."

Peter looked at him in shock, "Is he totally delusional?" Peter shouted.

Buckets put his arm around Peter and said, "Shut the fuck up."

Then, Bob addressing Peter again said, "I will write a cheque for the damages and your lost earnings."

The Cops, who knew Bob as well as the inevitable outcome of this situation, asked Peter, if he wanted to press charges. But, both Ram Jam and Bob, who were standing behind the Cops, started simultaneously shaking their heads at Peter, while Buckets of Blood, beside him, leant into his ear and whispered, "Say nothing."

As a consequence, Peter knew he had no other choice, and replied, "No, I don't want to press charges."

"So be it," the Cops said, and moved away.

Right after that, Buckets walked straight over to Bob and said, "Write a fucking cheque for two hundred fucking quid."

Peter just stood and said nothing.

Bob replied, "He would have to get a cheque back in the office."

Buckets, who was now facing Bob with a menacing face, spit as he spoke the words, "You fucking better, I know where you fucking live."

Bob asked Peter if he would drive him to the office and drop him home and Peter, still in shock, agreed.

Simultaneously, Ram Jam had filled John in on the events, who, in turn, relayed to the fleet.

"So, Peter picked up Tits Bob, he did his usual tit grope and got whacked over the head by the big tit girls' pimp, Peter's Window was put in, but the upside is, Peter, got two hundred quid and a flash of a nice set of tits."

Peter just looked out his broken window as he drove back to Bob's office.

Still traumatised by the entire situation, he didn't even feel how cold it was because of the lack of a window.

Bob was wincing in pain, obviously he was just coming down off adrenaline and whatever else he had taken.

After retrieving his cheque book and giving a cheque to Peter, Bob asked him to take him home to Donnybrook where his wife, who was standing near the gate, started screaming the moment she set eyes on him.

"What happened to you, my love?"

Bob replied, he had been a victim of another mugging.

His wife put her arms around him and said, "they keep picking on my big teddy bear."

Peter picked up his radio and said, "Driver 6, free in Donnybrook after dropping Tits Bob."

John, back to his usual self, replied, "Ahh, so you're familiar with Tits Bob, we'll make a Taxi Driver out of you yet."

Driver 34, "Donuts."

Gabriel got his name from the prostitutes who worked Fitzwilliam Square and Lad Lane.

Most Taxi Drivers knew all the girls that worked the streets and had a great rapport with them. Taxi Drivers from the old school, would bring them home for a ride or blowjob.

Gabriel allegedly had a kink where he liked the girls to place a donut on his cock and eat it, which of course, John had endless fun with.

When Gabriel called in to John when starting work, as he lived near the Base, John would ask him if he could get him a few Donuts for tea.

"Those ring donuts, you know the ones with the big ring, the fucking sugar goes everywhere, don't like the soggy ones."

Other drivers, joining in, would ask John, if he would require two or three donuts for a man of his size.

Runners always picked the older Taxi Drivers, considering them to be slow and unable to chase them.

Donuts was in his early sixties and had worked over thirty years in the Taxi business, he knew every trick and con, and was the definition of a hard man. He also carried a sawn-off shotgun under his seat for protection, nothing unusual back then, just like the secret switches beside the driver's right foot to disable the car, devices to render passengers needing a hospital, stun guns, Chinese police batons, bowie knives, chains, and an array of screwdrivers stuck in the air vent, all ready for use.

This story is about one poor fucker who tried to do a runner on Donuts, a twenty something year old, who was waiting across from the O' Connell Street Taxi Rank known as the main.

As soon as the first three Taxis got engaged, with younger drivers, he crossed and got into Donut's car.

Donuts had devised a pulley system in his car; all he had to do was pull a rope beside his right hand, it released a line of fishing line with two dozen hooks that he threw over the passenger.

The other drivers knew what the young fella was about, and so did Donuts who, driving off the taxi rank, made sure to put his window down and tell one of his friends that he was going fishing, with a big laugh.

His passenger didn't get the joke and asked where he was going fishing, but Donuts playing it cool, asked instead, "Where are you off to?"

"Clondalkin," his passenger replied.

"Then I'm going fishing in Clondalkin."

The young passenger hadn't a clue, kept making small talk all the way until he got to Neilstown, where he went quiet and limited the conversation to, "this left, this right."

As soon as Donuts slowed down, he held the rope in his hand ready to release. The passenger's door opened; the young fella smacked Donuts in the face as he tried to get out. But Donuts chose that moment to release the fishing line; the boy's body was snagged, his screams filled the car.

Donuts started to laugh; the passenger had all twelve fishing hooks in his shoulders and neck. Keying his mic, Donuts said, "Got myself a little mackerel, I think, John."

Donuts smiled into his passenger's face, now frozen in pain, any movement causing him more excruciating agony.

Then, pressing his finger into his passenger's shoulders, Donuts said, "You're a little Mackerel aren't yeah?"

His passenger was crying and begging Donuts, "Please man, please help me."

Donuts called in a code Charlie, to John, who knew all too well what Donuts was doing.

Meanwhile, Donuts had released the rope and held it like a dog lead. He told his passenger to get down on his fucking knees; but the boy was slow to react, so, Donuts pulled the rope to the ground forcing him to follow his instructions with cries.

Four taxis appeared beside Donut's car; John had, in fact, called the local taxi companies in Clondalkin for assistance. Now, all together, they were going to teach the little fucker a lesson, he would never forget.

First, they told him to strip, however, as he tried to remove his jeans in a doggy position, the hooks moved deeper into his skin.

The other drivers who were of the same age and mindset as Donuts, remained impassive to the scene as they too, had fallen victim and had been held up by young runners scumbags like that guy.

Donuts handed the rope to one of the taxi men and said, "Hold this!"

He took out his cock and pissed over his passenger's head, the acid in his urine burning into his cuts; Then, taking off his passenger's runners, they tied the laces together and chucked them over the electrical lines overhead, tied him up to a gate, and left him there.

"Shirley's Girls"

Back in the eighties, there was no support groups or help for Dublin's prostitutes as most of them were sent out to sell themselves by their own husbands or boyfriends, forced to have perverted and vile acts perpetrated against them nightly.

So, being raped or violently abused was part of their job description, just as returning home meant to be subjected to even more violence, more abuse. That's why they generally associated men with physical and mental pain, so debilitating, that every man was feared in equal measure.

Despite this, Driver 22, was considered a friend by all of Dublin's prostitutes. Being gay, he didn't pose a threat and he was not viewed as a potential punter. For them, he was just a former Priest driving a taxi around Dublin who from time to time, would pick up "his girls," as he fondly called them.

Besides, most still held fragments of their Catholic upbringing and feared that their souls were damned to hell.

Vincent removed their fears by introducing them to the stories of Our Lady and self-forgiveness, and, as a result, the girls called the Base in the small hours of the night asking for him, so that on the way from and to work, they could talk to him about the depraved, twisted acts some of their punters got them to perform, always asking at the end of their story if those sins would be forgiven.

Initially, what they revealed was shocking for a very shielded gay country young Irishman, but, eventually, he became desensitised to the perversion of man's desires by using humour.

As a matter of fact, he had a wicked sense of humour and was able to see the funny side of most situations; he called it his coping mechanism.

His girls would tease him about being gay by virtually demonstrating the act of giving a blowjob on a banana, giving him instructions on how to get a man to cum in seconds, where to and not to touch, secrets their punter's divulged, their punters idiosyncrasies, fantasies, from wearing nappies, pegs, or their mother's clothes to pissing on them or being pissed on.

Carrying over two dozen of his girls every week, the same stories were relived, like Taxi drivers, they too had nick names for themselves and their punters.

"Billy," was a punter, he wore a gold chain with what looked like a bell around his neck and because he liked being milked like a goat on all fours in the gardens of the Square.

"Sissy Steven," wore a French maid's uniform and liked being humiliated and having his ass spanked.

"Canister Charlotte," was a transvestite that worked the Square between midnight and three am, quite attractive, great figure, he used rubber balloons filled with oil as tits. He had a leather pencil holder he filled with engine oil that, once emptied, he used to give his punters the feeling of a wet pussy. He placed it between his legs as a vagina, while his cock and balls were strapped up between his ass with duct tape. Most of his punters were pissed and just wanted a quickie up against the wall, or a blowjob, never realising they were fucking a guy.

"The Duce," on the other hand, during her first night out on Fitzwilliam Square, had just finished counting her money, forty-two pounds when a fellow worker asked her, "Who gave you the two pounds?" and the Duce replied jokingly, "They all did."

"Black Babs," an English dominatrix who worked only the weekends on the Square, for the rest of the week, she worked in Tandies, a known brothel, in which she was valued for her speciality which was pegging, that's to say, the art of fucking her clients with a strap-on, torture and humiliation.

"Bad Pits" earned her nickname not because she was a traveller but because she reeked of sweat and wore the same skirt and coat for years.

"Double Up," had a sick perversion when on removing a condom from a Punter's cock; she would peel it off backwards letting all the cum flow over their pants and clothes, then, she would wash the condoms at a tap in a local petrol station and reuse them.

"Fingers," enjoyed to steal from her punters when they were fucking her, making her night if she found a wedding ring in their pocket, although, for whatever reason, some removed them before hooking up with the girls.

"Sniffles," was a junkie in her late teens that prostituted herself to feed her habit, working around Arbour Hill just beside Heuston Station, notorious for junkies.

"Dipso Debbie," always carried a bottle of Vodka in her bag to get through her night, and often, she would puke on a punter while they were fucking her, a habit which usually led her to ending up with a black eye or some broken ribs at the end of her night's work.

"Up The Bum Bernie," in order to get a guy to cum quicker she would stick her finger up his ass, wiping her finger in the middle of the back of his coat as a memento; an ongoing joke was when she finished with a punter and returned to the girls, they always asked her "how was he?" and she would always reply, "Shite."

Shirley knew nearly every working girl in Dublin, and he was intimately familiar with their life stories, how and why they started selling themselves for money, their toxic relationships and childhood abuses.

Nevertheless, throughout twenty years driving a taxi he used humour to numb the perversion of his and their reality. The following stories were told in graphic detail by women who had become conditioned to the abnormality of their lives and had nobody in the world to speak to.

Shirley was their confessional on wheels, their friend, and here are some of their incredible stories.

"The Mermaid"

Shirley first met Siobhan, "The Mermaid" in 1985, when she was a student in UCD. She was nineteen years old, studying medicine, and looking like a Greek Goddess with glistening black hair that touched her waist.

She was elegant and gracious, exquisitely beautiful, with a flawless complexion; her body was sculptured to an inch of the definition of femininity that oozed sensuality. She had captivating brown eyes that pierced, a distinctive addictive personality, the ability to make anyone feel very comfortable in her company.

Unlike the rest of her fellow students who were funded by rich parents, Siobhan funded her own college fees by being a "Companion" as she termed herself, charging men one hundred pounds for dinner, and two hundred and fifty for the full girlfriend experience. Most of her clients were rich and affluent and could afford to bestow gifts and money on her, dressing her in their desired outfits, paying her to fulfil their desires, a plaything for the wealthy.

One morning, Shirley was returning back from dropping off "Dipso Debbie" in Blanchardstown around five am, when a gentleman waved his taxi down in Castleknock, an affluent part of Dublin's Northside.

The guy was in his mid-fifties and spoke with a striking English accent, "Can you bring our friend back home, sir? she is heading to Monkstown."

Shirley was delighted with the return fare.

Siobhan got into the back seat of Shirley's Taxi and just like the gentleman she too, had a distinctive accent, this time an Irish one. "Monkstown please."

The first thing a Taxi Driver notices when a passenger gets into his car is their smell, being trapped in a six-foot square box, every sound is intensified, every smell is heightened, and in that moment, there was a pungent smell of semen coming from Siobhan, a smell Shirley knew all too well from carrying his girls.

Through his mirror he could see she was upset. "Are you okay?" he asked, adopting his camper accent that immediately removed any tension or fear for his female passengers.

"I'm okay, thank you for asking." Siobhan replied.

"Couldn't help but notice you're upset, being a gay guy, I know only too well about matters of the heart."

Siobhan looked up for the first time.

Now, he could see her face, "My, you are stunning, not my type though," making her smile.

"Would you mind if I cut through the Phoenix Park? it's quicker for the city," Shirley asked her.

She replied, "Yes that's perfect."

Ordinarily female passengers feared going through the Park with Taxi Drivers late at night, as there were many stories of women being assaulted; but that was not the case. By the time they came out of the Park onto Cunningham Road, Shirley had told her of his former profession being a Priest. Consequently, Siobhan opened up to him, telling him that she was a paid companion and that she was an Anniversary present for that gentleman and his wife back in Castleknock.

Shirley, never having heard of such a thing, replied, "That's a new one!"

Siobhan went on to tell him that it got a bit rough, and showed him, by raising her silk blouse the red marks across her abdomen.

"My, they look nasty, you poor thing, would you like to go to hospital?" he asked her.

She replied, "No, I will be okay."

"I would report them to the police, bloody terrible, who hit you?" Shirley asked.

"Everything was okay, I had dinner with them in Scott's Restaurant, they were very polite, innocent flirting about what we were going to do and things like that. During the drive back home, she kissed me, and he watched through his mirror. When we got back to their house, I saw pictures of their children, two girls about my age and a son, she asked me if I would role play. I told her, that I was theirs for the night. She got me to dress up like a prostitute in a black mini skirt, leather boots, and a tight t-shirt. She put red lipstick on me, told me to walk around and to follow her orders. Meanwhile, he sat in the seat just watching us. Then, she told me to crawl on my hands and knees, to raise my skirt so he could see my pussy, and to meow like a cat. She brought in a saucer of milk and told me to lick it up. As I was licking the milk, she ordered him to fuck me, so, he took out his cock. I tried to tell her I had to put a condom on his cock, but she said he wasn't one of my usual dirty bastards and that he was clean. I insisted, saying I didn't want to get pregnant, and she said *Okay*. But he started fucking me without it and cums in seconds; she laughed at him, called him a fucking pathetic ride, a little boy with a tiny cock, and then announced that it was her turn.

73

She took out some handcuffs and pushed me on the bed. She handcuffed my hands to chains that were already there, tied my legs apart, put a sock in my mouth and ripped my clothes off. After that, she started fingering my pussy roughly, she reached up behind the pillow and pulled out a huge cucumber and fucked me with it.

I started to cry in pain, but she just kept laughing at me. I was turning and twisting, trying to stop her and she just kept on fucking me. Then, she stripped and mounted the cucumber that was still half in me and fucked herself until she came. Afterwards, she asked him to fuck me again. I could see he hadn't a condom so I began to scream and shake my head, while she continued laughing and repeating in a little girl's voice. *I don't want to get pregnant; I don't want to get pregnant, fucking whore.*

Meanwhile, she was also intent on wanking him to get him hard again and told him to fuck my mouth; so he took out the sock and because I tried to tell them to stop, she punched me in the stomach and said, *Shut up you fucking whore!* He tried to fuck my mouth but I bit his cock. Taken aback by my reaction, he jumped off me while his wife, after calling him pathetic, started to pound my stomach with punches, and to punish me she fucked my mouth with the cucumber ramming it down my throat. I thought I was going to choke.

Later, she took a whip out and started to lash my breasts, asking me if I was going to bite him again, each lash deeper than the other. I eventually shook my head, he got back inside me, she took the cucumber, and after putting her hand between his legs, she placed it up my ass and started to fuck me, commanding him to fuck her, while saying, that she was filth, scum, a fucking dirty little whore who deserved to be treated like a dog, a fucking bitch dog. He came in me and rolled over.

She took out the cucumber from my ass and violently shoved it right up my pussy, and then put it down my throat. After that, she got up off the bed, went over to a dressing table, opened the drawer, took out a camera, and started taking pictures of me. I remember her saying *Look at you with a cucumber in your mouth and your pussy full of my husband's cum, you, fucking dirty whore.* Afterwards, she disappeared, and the husband, quickly opened the handcuffs, all the while apologising, blaming it on the cocaine they had taken earlier, repeating he would pay me double.

I still couldn't close my legs for the pain when she walked back into the bedroom fully dressed, told him to get rid of *that whore* from her house, saying *how dare he bring that thing back to her home*, and walked out of the room again. Finally, while I was getting dressed, he asked me if I wanted to shower, I refused, he gave me an extra two hundred and said he would destroy the pictures, that he couldn't talk to her right now, when she was in that state. Then you came along."

Shirley asked her again if she needed to go to the hospital, again she refused, saying that she wasn't too bad now, and that she would take a bath.

Then, Siobhan looked at Shirley and said, "Bet you never thought that was my reason for being upset."

He replied, "Believe me I've heard much, much, worse."

Curious he asked her, "Where were the children when this was all going on?"

She told him there seemed to be nobody else in the house and that she had been a plaything for couples before but never had she experienced such violence, particularly from a woman.

And that was the start of Shirley and the Mermaid's relationship, bringing her to and from clients like his other girls, divulging the events of her nights.

One of George's Threesomes!

Trying to make money was George's biggest problem. Half, if not most of his night were usually spent in the attempt to refuse the advances of some female admirers or gay guys, something that meant losing ten to fifteen minutes on some fares trying to get them out of his taxi or avoiding certain passengers. George found out quickly that politeness didn't work, and that rudeness could create even more problems; so, he eventually came up with an idea: every time a woman tried to come onto him, he would declare he was gay.

In the beginning, he told them he was married, but he soon discovered that the information worked as an aphrodisiac for them because it was like admitting that in addition to being drop dead gorgeous, he was also experienced. To the gay guys, on the other hand, George would generally say that he was married and straight, but regardless of that, his passengers wanted to convert him.

George always left his mic open for John to hear the desperate ones as he would tease them, the excuses he made up for them like that he had to work, or the offers of money he got for his company. Sometimes, he would indulge his clients by asking them what they wished him to do to them, or what their fantasies were; these were mostly coy but quite graphic.

A female caller from Rathfarnham was one of those forceful passengers; she called the Base one Sunday evening looking for George to bring her into town.

"Drivers 69, have one of your sisters on, here, from Rathfarnham looking for you."

In that moment, George couldn't remember her but headed over to collect her. However, when he got outside her door he remembered.

Only a week earlier, he struggled to get her out of his car, she and two of her friends, three thirtysomething years old who behaved like dogs in heat, feeling his chest and groping his crotch as he drove them back from a drunken girl's night out.

As each of them got to their house they wouldn't get out unless he kissed them, which was not just a peck as their drunken tongues, laced with kebab-breath, went down the back of his throat.

When he finally arrived at the house of the last one, where he was now parked outside, she asked for more than just a kiss. George would have fucked her, if it were not for the day, Saturday, the busiest night of the week. So, he used every excuse he could think of, and in the end, he relied on John to get her out.

George blew into the Base he was "stuck in Rathfarnham" which was a code for - can't get this one out. And John, knowing all too well how valuable every hour on a Saturday night was, called Driver 69 back and told him, to get down to Rathmines immediately or else he would have to report him.

At last, she reluctantly accepted to be left alone, but only after making George promise to hook up again with her.

So, now, here she was again. She quickly opened his front passenger door and got in beside George; something unusual considering that the ninety nine percent of women back then, would normally get in the back of a taxi when they were on their own.

"Hello again," she said, all smiles, "Do you remember me? I'm Vicky."

"Yes, you were.." George hesitated, then he noticed her wedding ring, something he didn't see the last time she travelled with him. "..You weren't married the last time I had seen you," he replied.

"Aren't you the observant one?" she said now flirting with him. "Where do you want to take me?" she asked smiling.

George keyed his mic for John to hear and said loudly "Where would I like to take you? from behind.." George replied.

She smiled, moved close to him, she reached over and placed her hands between his legs. Her face now was beside his, "Wow, you're certainly cocky in every way." She kissed the side of his neck as she continued caressing his groin, her perfume added to her femininity something George had a weakness for.

For John's entertainment, George asked her loudly what she wanted to do.

"I want to fuck you silly."

He smiled and said, "Say that again, this time slowly." George was still driving towards the city centre, "Are we still heading into town?" he asked.

"Yes, having dinner with my boring husband, he would love to see you fuck me."

George got even harder with that thought, so, she zipped his jeans and took out his growing cock. Her eyes were showing her surprise as she said, "Wow, that's some cock, its fucking huge, bet you're told that a lot."

George replied, "Every time" with a big smile on his face.

79

In broad daylight on Rathgar Road, she went down on George, and again for John's entertainment, George said, "Suck it hard, I love the sound of slurping, bite it."

She kept sucking him, beavering, and vacuuming him like an Olympic champion, until, while going over Rathmines Bridge, he exploded into her mouth.

After that, she came up and showed him her tongue with his cum and swallowed it.

"Did you like that?" she asked him.

His cock was getting hard again.

"Oh, I can see you certainly did," she smiled, looking at his cock getting bigger. "We will have to put that away for now" she bent down and wrapped her tongue around it again, whispering, "I will see you later," she placed his cock back into his pants and patted it.

"Are you going to collect me later?" she asked.

"Absolutely," George replied.

George blew in, "Driver 69, free in town."

John replied, "Doing the devils work on a Sunday Driver 69? I'm just watching a programme about vegetarians. I say there's nothing better than a good meat eater, would you agree with that Driver 69?"

George replied, "Only the ones who chew and swallow."

The witching hour in the taxi business was between eleven thirty and four am, as that was when the pubs and nightclubs ended. They were the most valued hours, and the ones a driver couldn't afford to lose.

Just coming up to midnight, John called Driver 69. "Have your sister on here, are you free to pick her and her hubby up on Wicklow Street? It's the same restaurant you dropped at earlier, remember the time Driver 69."

George replied, "Will call you when finished, don't think I will be that long."

George pulled outside the restaurant where Vicky and her husband were waiting; they both got into the back seat.

Vicky's husband spoke first. "Hi, I'm Robert, I believe your hung like a horse."

A startled George replied to him, "Who told you that?"

"My little cock sucker beside me, well I guess she is a big cock sucker now." He put his arm around her, "Vicky certainly loves the Micky."

Vicky and Robert laughed, then kissed.

George didn't know what to think. While he had fucked hundreds of married women, this situation was bizarre. George was extremely confident and didn't get intimidated easily. George was built like a shithouse and had practised martial arts for years.

The journey back to Rathfarnham was quick and when they got outside, Vicky's husband got out leaving her, "That was strange," George commented.

Vicky replied, "Ahh, that's just my little bitch, are you going to come in?"

"Is he okay with this?" George asked her.

"Fucking yes, he's fucking dying for it," Vicky replied. She leaned in between the seats and kissed him, whispering in his ear, "I'm fucking gagging for you too."

George turned around facing her and said, "What are you both into?"

She replied, "He is BI and gets off looking at me being fucked, he has a fetish about my clothes, so he's probably getting dressed right now in my underwear, are you okay with that?"

George thought about it, and said, "Sure, I don't care as long as I can fuck you and he's not fucking me. That's a, no-no, okay?" he said.

They both got out of the car and walked into the house. Just as they walked in, Vicky's husband was coming down the stairs in her bright pink knickers and bra. George was frantically trying not to laugh.

"This is Robyn," Vicky introduced him by his preferred female name.

"Hi, Robyn," George replied.

Vicky told George to jump up on the counter in the middle of the kitchen, which George did. Vicky unzipped his jeans and took out his cock.

"Oh my God," Robyn said in her sudo female voice, "It's bigger than you said. How will you get that in your mouth?"

"Like this," Vicky grabbed his cock and mouthed George's.

Robyn stood looking at Vicky vacuuming George's cock; Robyn asked him if she could suck him too. George replied, he wasn't into Guys.

Vicky came up off George's cock and said, "Robyn, give George two hundred pounds and I'm sure he will let you suck him."

George thought about it, two hundred quid was nearly a week's work, George answered by saying, "I'm not fucking you."

Vicky answered, "No, that's my pleasure".

George reached out his hand and gestured for the money, as Vicky went back down on him, Robyn returned with the money and handed it to George.

She walked around beside Vicky and said, "Can I have a go?"

Vicky replied, he likes this, sticking out her tongue, she flipped it over the head of George's cock, back and forth, and forced it down the whole of George's cock.

Robyn said, "God, it's even bigger up close," as Vicky grabbed Robyn's head shoving it down and said, "Suck that cock you little fucking bitch, suck it while I fuck you, play with his balls." Vicky opened a drawer and took out a black leather strap on.

She undressed behind Robyn who was giving even better head than Vicky did. George was sitting enjoying both the blowjob and the striptease.

Vicky now naked, stepped into the strap on and tightened the leather straps, pulling Robyn's knickers down, letting her saliva drip on the top of the rubber cock, she looked at George and smiled, blowing him a kiss and inserted it into Robyn's ass. Robyn winced as Vicky penetrated him.

"This is my little bitch," Vicky informed George who was enjoying every second.

Vicky got into character and started to fuck her bitch harder and harder, vocalising everything she was doing, telling Robyn to suck that big cock, to get it right down his throat, and gag. She told George to get up and fuck her from behind.

Robyn was now bent over the counter.

George stood up, his cock standing to attention, as he walked behind Vicky, her ass tight, he pulled back her G-string and pushed his cock deep into her wet pussy, cupped her soft tits with his hands and joined her physical rhythm as she penetrated Robyn.

Vicky was enjoying George's cock too much and shouted, "Does my little bitch need to cum?"

Robyn replied, "Oh yes, yes, please."

Vicky reached around Robyn's waist and grabbing his cock, she started to wank him off, while still fucking him. Within seconds, his cum was on the floor.

"Lick that up you little bitch, right now!"

Robyn obeyed her order, bent down, and licked up his own cum. Then, Vicky turned around, stepped out of the strap-on, and slowly undressed George, all the while ogling his physique.

George picked her up, placed her on the counter, and pulling her legs apart, he went down on her. His tongue was like an electric fan as it flipped over her g-spot, licking and fingering her.

Through sighs, Vicky barely managed to order Robyn to suck George's cock, before screaming in ecstasy as she orgasmed.

"I've just started with you." George said. He picked her up off the counter and placed her onto all fours, her face looking up at Robyn who was standing right in front of them.

George was now fucking her doggy style.
"You like looking at your wife being fucked, don't you Robyn?"

Vicky asked through sighs and gasps.

Robyn replied, "Yes."

George flipped her over on her back on the floor and started to pound her deeper, Robyn's eyes transfixed on George's tight ass as it penetrated Vicky, she climaxed and came, George exploded inside her.

"Come over here and clean us up," Vicky directed Robyn. "It's clean up time; you know how you like to clean up."

Robyn started with George first, sucking and licking his balls and cock clean; then she got in between Vicky's legs and licked her.

"Now go to bed," Vicky ordered Robyn, "We want to fuck some more."

By three thirty am, George was showered and dressed. He was just about to leave when Vicky, asked him if he wanted to make it a regular thing.

George replied, "Plus the two hundred."

Vicky answered with a big smile, "Most definitely, you're worth every penny and after all, it's my generous husband who's paying."

The first thing George did when he got back into his car was key his mic Driver 69 just back in.

"I sold that fishing rod for two hundred, good night's work." Sarcastically he said, "Unfortunately someone has to do it."

John replied, "Hate the smell of fish."

Gorgeous George spent a lot of time visiting Rathfarnham over the following months. Vicky's sexual appetite expanded with every encounter, together with her cocaine habit. George's physical stamina and sexual prowess enchanted her.

Birthday, Christmas and Anniversary presents were all bought in adult stores, toys, chains, and whips for Robyn. Later, when Robert was away working Vicky told George she wanted to break their rule; however, it was agreed between Robert and Vicky, no fucking unless together.

"Nuts and Daniel O' Donnell"

Buckets of Blood was always scheming and scam-ming, from robbing passengers' duty-free, to dipping their pockets when he used the heater trick.

Having fallen for Nuts madness, he saw a way of mak-ing a lot of money from his talent. Daniel O' Donnell was organising a concert in the Point Depot, which guaran-teed Buckets a lot of potential victims.

Buckets would sell tea sets pretending they were from Daniels mother's house, stockings, even jumpers, any shite he could sell as memorabilia.

His plan was to get Nuts "AKA," Daniel O' Donnell, to speak to them on the phone. Nuts could do any accent so all he had to do was get a phone close enough to the Point Depot that he could use.

A pub called Kavanaghs, three doors from the point depot, had a phone; the only problem was it was in the bar. Buckets wrote out a script with thirty-five words on a large piece of white cardboard for Nuts to follow.

In big black letters, it read, "Hello, what's your name, that's a beautiful name, thank you for attending my con-cert and God bless you. I'm so sorry I have to run, hope you have a great night, goodbye for now."

Buckets had organised Nuts to be up in the Base when he rang, while John was there to make sure everything went smoothly.

Daniel O' Donnell concerts attracted mainly women with strong Christian beliefs, mostly from the country-side, very trusting and very naive when it came to dealing with city people known as Dubs like Buckets.

It wasn't unusual for them to queue for six to seven hours to guarantee they would get their position directly in front of the stage, so they could admire Daniel and display their homemade signs, advocating their undying love for him.

Buckets parked on the Abbey Street taxi rank that was the busiest on a concert night; it was five twenty when his first fare got in. It was two big countrywomen or country bumpkins, as Buckets called them. Buckets' dashboard had been turned into a Daniel O' Donnell shrine, with mugs with his picture, plates, tie pins and buntings.

After turning off Abbey Street, he started with his spiel about his brother working as Daniel's bodyguard and that he could get them to speak to Daniel if they liked. Obviously, his brother was risking his job so they would have to make it worth his while.

Hooked, he parked his car with the taxi meter still running and brought them into the pub, where the locals started looking at them over their pints of Guinness, as it was totally unusual back then for a woman to set foot in a bar.

Ladies only drank in the lounge. Buckets dialled the Base, John answered and hearing Buckets voice, said, "Hello, this is Daniel O' Donnell's dressing room." Buckets handed over the receiver and the two women held it between their ears, all giddy and excited like two teenagers.

One of them said, "Could we speak to Daniel if that's okay?"

John high on blow handed the phone to Nuts, who was also high on blow, saying, "Daniel, it's for you."

John keyed the mic so the other drivers could hear Nuts impersonations; it was so perfect some of the other Daniel O' Donnell concert goers in Kilmore taxis thought it was him too, screaming their heads off.

"It's Daniel, its Daniel."

Buckets watched as the two started to scream "Daniel, we love you; it's Mary and Biddy from Offaly."

Nuts, of course, ignored the script, much to John's delight and said, "Hello Mary and Biddy, isn't that beu -titful names, are yee coming to see me tonight?"

Biddy shouted her reply, "We're coming Daniel, just for you."

One of the old guys in the bar said, "That's the reason women are not allowed in bars, dirty disgusting bitches."

Nuts and John were laughing like schoolboys. Nuts asked them if they were good girls.

They replied again, shouting their reply, "Yes, we are good girls."

Buckets grabbed the phone saying, "Sorry girls that's all the time we have," hanging up.

Outside the Point Depot, his taximeter was reading ten pounds, which was five pounds more than it should be. The two women, still on a high after talking to their hero, asked him how much they owed, "Let's call it twenty, I'll look after my brother," they looked at each other in shock but paid and got out.

Later on, Buckets went straight back into the bar and rang John.

"What's that fucking egit doing? Get him to stick to the fucking script for fucksake!" Buckets slammed down the phone.

89

The next fare was a woman on her own, Buckets di-alled in and handed her the phone.

She said, "Hello, this is Philomena from Waterford, is that Daniel?"

Nuts replied, "Well hello, Phil-o-me-n-a from Water-ford, it's so nice of yee to be call-n me, I'm just finishing a nice cup of tea and was going to say a prayer of the rosary, would you join me Philomena? Let's get down on our knees and pray, it doesn't matter where we are, we have to kneel for Our Lord."

John spat out his tea, Philomena in the crowded pub full of men, kneeled down and started the rosary saying, "Hail Mary Full of Grace."

Everyone in the bar thought she was some religious psycho.

Nuts said, "I can't hear you Phil-o-me-n-a, shout to the Lord," she screamed, "I will Daniel, I will."

Buckets grabbed the phone off her saying the time was up, again overcharging her for the fare and an extra ten pounds for talking to Daniel.

Buckets rang the Base again, spitting fire, telling John to put Nuts on the phone.

John handed Nuts the phone and said, "It's for you." Nuts answered as Daniel, with "Hello, what's your name?"

Buckets answered, "I'll tell you my fucking name, I will ram my fucking fist down your fucking throat, now stick to the script" again slamming down the phone.

John said to Nuts, "Guess he's not a Daniel O' Don-nell fan." The two of them laughed their heads off again, by the third call Nuts and John were stoned, John handed Nuts the phone and said, "Mr Paisley, it's for you."

Nuts went into a staunch Ian Paisley voice and said, "Who's this?"

A timid voice on the other end said, "It's Theresa."

Nuts answered again as Ian, "What's a Finnian bitch ringing me for?"

Theresa, shocked, replied, "I would like to speak to Daniel."

Ian called Daniel, "Hey buttfuck it's for you."

The entire fleet was in stitches; John was rolling on the ground holding his stomach.

Buckets grabbed the phone just as Nuts said in a perfect Daniel O' Donnell accent, "Well, hello Theresa, that's a lovely name"

Buckets gave her back the phone and said, "It's Daniel."

Nuts finished the call to the script; Buckets got paid, returning to the rank for another victim.

On the fourth call John gave Nuts the phone. Daniel said, "Hello, who's pissed?" John and Nuts started to laugh again.

The voice said "Sorry, I'm Isabelle."

Daniel replied "Is-a-bell necessary on a bike, did you ever hear that one before Isabelle?" she laughed and said "Yes," she used to be teased when she was a wee child.

Buckets face was getting redder with temper listening to her replies.

Daniel said to Isabelle, "Do you know who's here with me right now?"

Isabelle answered, "No, who?"

He replied, "I give him the phone and see if yee can guess."

Cliff Richard said, "Hello, is this Isabelle?" Nuts started to sing, "We're all going on a summer holiday, no more working for a week or two."

Standing in the pub, she started to jump up and down, she screamed into the phone "It's Cliff Richard!" Then, turning to Buckets she screamed again, "It's Cliff Richard!"

Buckets put his hands over his face, rolled his eyes, and waited another five minutes for the call to end.

Anyway, his patience was rewarded when, after asking her for twenty pound she kissed him on the side of the face and said, "Here's thirty, that's the best thing that has ever happened to me in my life, imagine, I spoke to Daniel O' Donnell and Cliff Richard, nobody would ever believe me."

Buckets replied, "Yeah your right, nobody would ever believe you."

John told Nuts that, at seven thirty that would probably be the last fare. So, picking up the phone Nuts prepared to impersonate once again Daniel "Hello, who's this?"

Three voices screaming down the phone in the thickest Cork accents said, "It's your biggest Cork fans!"

Daniel replied, "No, I think the girls from Tyrone are, sure they're great craic."

One of the voices replied, "We're better craic."

Daniel asked them to prove it by dancing with yer man beside them, swing him around.

The receiver dropped, and they could hear Buckets voice saying, "Would you fuckoff, I don't want to dance."

Twenty minutes later, Buckets blew into John and said, "I'm on my way up to the Base to that fucking little bollox to knock the shit out of him."

Nuts keyed the mic and replied, in a Frank Spencer voice, "Oh Betty, I think I'm in trouble. Buckets done a whoopsie in the Garden."

Nuts wasn't there when he got to the Base, but Buckets did leave him twenty quid…

Gorgeous George and the Full Boyfriend Experience

In a time before internet, or social media, where the only forms of communication were telephone calls and letters, advertisement was done in a book called the yellow pages. Irish society was conditioned and governed by the Catholic Church and sex was a taboo subject, never spoken freely about. Most considered it a duty to be performed for procreation.

On one occasion, one of Siobhan's male clients asked her if she could find him a male equivalent for his sister. She was on the other side of forty, recently deserted by her husband for a twenty-something year old. She wanted no strings attached sex, the full boyfriend experience without the drama. Siobhan didn't want to disappoint her male client who had been extremely generous to her. None of the guys she knew in college could be trusted. She knew that if she told any of them, her secret would be exposed, and her life would be ruined.

Some nights later, Siobhan called for Shirley Driver 22 to pick her up and bring her to a client's apartment in Foxrock. On the way, she asked him if he knew any good-looking fit guy that wasn't gay and who would be up for some paid fun with an elegant older woman.

Straight away Shirley thought of Gorgeous George, and began describing him to Siobhan, who immediately sensed how much Shirley liked him, his mouth almost salivating as he listed George's attributes.

So, Siobhan asked him if he could arrange for her to meet George for coffee and Shirley, although he didn't want to ask George, in the end, he convinced himself as

Siobhan was one of his girls and he would do anything for them.

Biting the bullet, he followed George onto a Taxi rank and uncharacteristically got into his car.

George turned around and said, "Hello, Shirley."

He could feel his heart race. "Hi, I'm Vincent, Driver 22, but John calls me Shirley."

George replied still smiling, "Yes, I know."

Shirley trying to be extremely diplomatic, said, "I have a girlfriend who is looking for a good-looking guy, that's you, that box is certainly ticked, for some paid fun, is that something you would be interested in?"

George smiled and asked, "How much is she offering?"

Shirley replied, "Two hundred and fifty pounds."

George, still smiling said, "Worth having a coffee, so I guess."

Three days later, George met Siobhan in a coffee shop in Ringsend; she was already there, and when he walked in, thanks to the description Shirley gave of George, she recognised him right away. She stood up to greet him.

"You are even more handsome than Shirley mentioned," Siobhan said, still smiling at George.

"Could say the same about you too," he responded.

"Okay, I guess Shirley has told you about me and what I do."

"Actually, he hasn't," George was quick to correct her.

"Oh, that's good," Siobhan replied. "Let's say I connect people. My connection wants someone like you to make their life fun and exciting."

George replied, smiling "Would that be adult fun?"

Siobhan smiled back and said, "You catch on quick. There is a lady in her forties, quite attractive for her age, who wants no strings attached adult fun. She will pay you two hundred and fifty pounds for a night's entertainment, she obviously will want to meet you briefly and if she's happy with you, which I certainly know she will be," again she smiled at George, "and that's it."

George responded, "Okay set it up. It wouldn't hurt to have coffee, I'm not really into that age, but hey, if we gel it's good."

Siobhan asked George if he had a girlfriend, already knowing the answer from Shirley, George shook his head, and said, "I never limit myself to one, when I can have fun with them all."

"So not boyfriend material, I guess," Siobhan replied.

George turned on his charm. Within ten minutes the two of them were laughing like old friends, three hours later George got out of Siobhan's bed, she looked at his naked body and said, "God, she will certainly be one happy lady, do what you just did to me, and she will give you anything."

George returned and bent over the bed and kissed her. "Do you think I'm really worth it?" his eyes quizzing her playfully.

She grabbed his cock, and said, "There's not a woman in Ireland who wouldn't give their weeks earnings for that." Bringing her mouth onto his, kissing him gently, she said, "and that wicked tongue of yours, wow, you are certainly orally gifted, if I could pimp you out day and night, we could make a fortune."

He grabbed her, rolling around on the bed as they both laughed. Siobhan said she would organise the meeting, probably in the Dalkey Island Hotel and she would let Shirley know; they kissed and after that, George left her apartment.

By the end of the week, George was walking into the Dalkey Island hotel at seven thirty as organised, wearing tight black jeans and a loose-fitting white cotton shirt. He scanned the lobby, but there was no sign of anyone.

He tried the restaurant where he saw a couple having drinks. He thought to himself that maybe she was running late, so he ordered a glass of water.

Ten minutes later a waiter came over to him and said, "Your friend won't be able to meet this evening, she sends her apologies." George paid for the drink and left, thinking she obviously got cold feet. George considered it a bit of fun but realised for someone not so open minded it might be difficult.

Only by chance he picked up a fare at the Queens pub in Dalkey Village going to Monkstown. By the time he dropped the couple, Arthur called him and asked if he could go back to the hotel, that he had left something behind. George knew Arthur was speaking code so no-one else would realise what was going on.

Nevertheless, fifteen minutes later George arrived back in the car park of the Dalkey Island Hotel, and just as he was about to get out, a woman opened his passenger door and got in.

"Hello, I'm Karen." George looked at her, she was quite attractive for her age, not too made up, wearing an exquisite dress, her perfume rich and musky, her hair in a bun. Looking at her, he considered she must have been quite beautiful, twenty years earlier.

He reached out his hand and shook hers. "Hi, I'm George, so nice to meet you," he replied.

"You must forgive me; I have never done anything like this before," she replied.

George interrupted her by saying, "Karen, you don't have to explain or apologise, we are just two adults talking, maybe having coffee, would you like one?" he asked her.

Karen smiled, and said, "I live across the road, would you like to have coffee there or here? whatever you feel okay with."

George replied, "I'm here for you, so we'll do whatever makes you comfortable."

"Okay, let's have it in mine, you can leave your car here and we can walk over, it's just there," Karen replied. pointing her finger across the road.

Karen's home was literally a mansion; and George was extremely charming and chivalrous pulling out her seat for her to sit down, complementing her attire all the while, sitting very comfortably in the seat next to her.

Karen focused on making small talk about her passion for art, and George indulged her by asking, "What attracts you to certain paintings?"

She replied, "Mostly colours, or how the light makes an image change."

George got up and walked over to a painting on her wall, and looking up at it with his back to her, he asked, "How do great artists become great?"

Karen looked over at him smiling, she replied, "Years of experience, and a God-given talent."

George still studying the picture, responded, "Isn't it amazing how, despite the fact sexuality is one of the most intimate aspects of humans, it's never investigated, never explored, never learned, and sadly most are not even interested in understanding it, too selfish I guess."

Karen got up off her seat, walked over to him, and said, "I was certainly not expecting that."

Suddenly, he turned, looked at her, and with his fingertips, he started touching her inner arms, and while caressing them, he asked "Do you know the body has over thirty erogenous zones?" George reached down her long arms and lightly stroked the back of her knee, "Like there," still looking at her, his hands running up the outside of her dress, his fingers softly touching her inner thighs. "Like there too," he smiled, kissing her lips.
"There as well," deliberately avoiding her groin his fingers slid along the material of her dress across to the top of her naval, momentarily stopping circling with his fingers, he looked at her again and said, "There as well." Bending, kissing her neck, he whispered "and there."

Then, he kissed her just behind her ear as his fingers slowly glanced over her nipples; Karen's body now started responding to his touch like electricity. "Like there," George smiled, as he caressed her face and said, "It takes patience and control, but most of all it takes the willingness to discard everything you thought you knew about your body. Intimacy, sexual fulfilment are not just physical they're mental and the two need to be satisfied simultaneously."

Karen smiled and said, "Wow, where did you learn how to do that?"

Still holding her by the waist, her body now gravitating to him, he replied with such intensity "Making love is like making wine, it takes years of experience, knowing where to touch, how soft or hard to caress. Opening a body and mind to a new world of pleasure, it's exactly like wine, what fruits to choose, never rushing, having the patience to wait to enjoy your lover's taste, knowing how to extract the very last drop from her."

Karen smiled up at him and said, "Wow, haven't heard that from any man in my life, normally it's a quick grab of my tits, Wham! Bam! thank you ma'am, and he is done." She looked at him and said, "You don't know me, I'm a stranger."

He brought her down to the carpet, and spoke softly, "We are all strangers, do we really know anyone? know their thoughts, know their fantasies, what they really feel, every one of us pretends, act the way we feel others expect, trying to make everyone else happy, it's okay to let yourself go, be selfish, allow time for you."

He leaned into her and kissed her passionately. His arms now were placed around her body holding her.

Karen looked up at him and said, "I haven't kissed like that since I was a teenager."

George caressed her face and moved back her hair and said, "Would you like to get to know you?"

Karen looked puzzled, replying, "I certainly would like to get to know you, but I already know myself."

George gently caressed her left arm while still staring at her, he said softly, "The you, that you have become, is not, the you that will wake up in the morning."

Karen wasn't expecting George to be so philosophical and good looking.

"Wow," she said, "Do you think you could change me that much in one night?"

He looked at her and said, "If you leave all your inhibitions, forget your past experiences, ignore time, allow me to explore you, then, I guarantee you that you will wake up a different person."

She stood up; George could sense her apprehension.

"I know you are nervous, it's natural, we can go as slow as you like, or we can still have coffee."

George had practised martial arts for over fifteen years together with trans meditation and loved taking things very slowly. He was extraordinarily laidback; he leaned over and gently kissed her. "Would you like me to give you a massage?" he asked her.

Karen laughed. "Wow, you certainly are not like any man I know."

George replied, "Hopefully that's a good thing."

She nodded her head.

"So, would you like me to massage you? just a massage, nothing else," George asked her again.

She looked at him, he could see she was nervous, for the first time, she dropped her facade and said, "I hate my body, I had three kids and it's not like the girls you probably know, it's disgusting. My husband and I had sex in the dark and it only ever lasted a couple of minutes, most times I would have to masturbate myself after he went asleep."

George put his arm around her pulling her close to him, looking into her eyes, he said, "What a terrible waste." His fingers gently brushed back her hair from her face, he said, "You are beautiful, he was a fool to lose you, and you are extremely attractive, you could have a line of guys queuing for you."

Karen looked at him and said, "Don't want another re-lationship, some guy who wants to use me. I just want fun, to be happy, I have had enough drama for one life."

"What helps your blank things out?" George asked her.

She looked at him, her voice gently and soft as she replied, "I listen to music, sometimes I get lost in it."

George kissed her and said, "Okay, let's turn up the music and I will give you a massage. Afterwards, I will make you a cocktail, do you have body oil and some-where I can massage you? I call it getting to know the sensual points."

Karen responded, "Do we talk about money?"

George put his finger to her mouth and shook his head, saying, "If tomorrow you don't feel like a different woman you don't have to pay me anything."

She took him by the hand and led him into the gym room where there was a physio table; she pointed at a cabinet where the body oils were stored, she pressed play on the CD player and Kenny G's, Song Bird started to play. She disappeared into a room and returned wearing a bathrobe over a towel.

Taking off the robe she lay down on her stomach, opening the towel which covered her body.

George slowly folded it neatly back across her butt. He took some oil and rubbed it into his hands and started to massage her shoulders, his fingers sliding across her skin, focusing on her tightened muscles.

"You have great hands," she told him.

He continued massaging her back, he could feel her body starting to relax, the tension was slowly disappear-ing from her. His fingers every now and then, would slip under her towel caressing her butt, and in those moments, he could see her body raise almost inviting his fingers in. Before taking off his shirt, he asked her if it was okay, and she nodded her agreement.

Her eyes never stopped gazing at his reflection in the mirrors that circled the room, even when he continued massaging her lower back, watching in turn her body move every time the tips of his fingers slipped between her cheeks. Later, his hands moved down to her right foot massaging it right up to her thigh, moving across to her left, his fingers touching her, as her body kept reacting to his fingers until she started to moan.

George asked her if she would mind if he took off her underwear to massage her properly and she shook her head. Her eyes were closed but she continued smiling as he reached under the towel with two fingers of each hand pulling her knickers slowly down off her butt and across her thighs, always careful to touch her skin in order to let the sensations to spread across all of her body. Slowly, her knickers passed the back of her knees and another wave of pleasure flowed inside her.

His hands returned to work on her body; now he could see her pussy as his hand slid open her cheeks, tipping it every so often almost as if it was by accident. He could see the muscles around her groin tense and then relax.

One moment, she tried to turn around, but he gently pressed her body, and bending down to her ear, he said "You are like art, let me show you how wonderful it is, learning every sensual part of your body, every erogenous zone, every fibre and sensual point, what turns you on.. just relax and allow me to awaken your sexual being." So, he kept massaging her, his hands now were moving across her butt, his fingers disappeared between her cheeks, parting them, his middle finger gently caressed her pussy. She moaned with each touch, very slowly he opened her legs apart as he massaged her inner thighs. Karen tried to say something; he asked her if she was enjoying what he was doing; she smiled and said, "I'm in heaven."

Just with his fingertips, he caressed the inside of her legs, starting at her knees, moving up slowly, caressing her pussy, squeezing her butt. He could see the blood flowing between her legs, her lips now bright pink, her scent filling George's nostrils. He smiled, savouring her aroma, her body twitching as he stroked her, as she sighed louder; he opened her legs wider and started to lick her lightly.

She whispered, "I'm not into that," he replied, "Try it, concentrate on the music, focus on the sensation." George said softly into her ear.

His tongue caressing every inch of her inner thighs, as his fingers gently flipped back and forth across her clit lips. Her body tensed ready to orgasm, he stopped, she looked at him, puzzled, he bent down and kissed her and said, "I will teach your body how to build an orgasm, teasing, manipulating your desires, your sexual desperation will explode and flow."

His fingers returned to her inner thighs moving them to her pussy, she closed her eyes, his tongue kissed the lower part of her back, travelling down to her butt, sliding down between her cheeks, his fingers massaged her pussy, his head now firmly between her legs, she could feel his hot breath, as he opened her gently and replaced his finger that was circling her g-spot with his tongue, blowing gently, lightly sucking her.

Humming so the vibration would travel inside her, as her thighs tightened, he sucked deeper, flipping his tongue rhythmically over her g-spot. Then, his hands travelled up to her breasts and nipples caressing them, her thighs tightening around his head, her body about to cum.

The moment he curved his tongue and licked her deep inside, her hot cum gushed into his mouth as he consumed her; he swallowed every drop while her body lifted off the table uncontrollably with each spasm that followed, and her moans filled the room.

Trying to catch her breath, she turned around to look at him, and attempting to cover herself with the towel, she said "I have never experienced anything like that before, it was like nothing I've ever felt," she started to laugh and screamed, "It was bloody incredible!"

He bent down to her and replied, "Would you like to learn how to make love now?"

She looked at him with a shocked look, and replied, "What was that then?"

He smiled and said, "Foreplay."

"I don't know if I can, I'm exhausted," Karen replied.

He kissed her softly, then more intense until both of them were lost in their passion. George's hands caressed the sides of her breasts, teasing her nipples, going down on her again, and when he came back up, he unzipped his jeans, took them off so she could see his cock sticking out above his pants.

"My, wow, I have never seen a penis like that before."

Grabbing his jeans, he took out a condom and put it on. He smiled, and leaning back down, continued to kiss her passionately, his cock rubbing off her pussy, slowly finding its way into her. Her nails dug into his ass as he pushed the top of it in and out of her wet pussy, opening her wider inside as he penetrated her gently. Her sighs and moans were getting louder, her eyes opened wider as he trusted deeper. He had still his head between her breasts and his lips were sucking her nipples, when her body tightened, released again, and she orgasmed with a big sigh, collapsing back onto the table.

He went down on her again, she tried to stop him, saying, "It's messy down there."

He smiled and said, "That's the wine I made, now I am going to consume it." He sucked and licked every part of her pussy. Looking up at her, he could see she was smiling, enjoying this new sensation.

Coming back up, she asked him if he came.

He shook his head, and said, "That's not important, watching your body rise off the table is my orgasm, knowing I made you feel that."

Sitting up on the table, she reached out for his hand but instead she grabbed his standing cock and peeling off his condom, she started to masturbate him.

He removed her hand and said, "Have you ever seen a man wackoff before?"

She shook her head; "Let me show you how horny you have made me. I want to show you my desperation, my desire for you." So, he wrapped his hand around his cock and started pulling it, up and down, slowly, and as its head was growing bigger, he placed the finger of his other hand under his balls.

Her eyes were now transfixed on the head of his cock, her smile widening every time his hand jerked. She could see his desperation as he exploded over her legs and onto the table.

Later, he bent down and kissed her. She looked at him and said, "I'm forty-five years old and have never experienced anything like this in my life. My God, you are a sex artist with God-given talents."

They both laughed as he drew her close hugging her as his tongue explored her mouth again kissing her passionately. Then, he said, "That's just your first lesson Karen."

"First of many I hope," she replied.

"What about that cocktail?" she asked him laughing.

He walked into the kitchen still naked and returned with a towel being carried by his erect cock.

"There's my cock," he turned around and said, "There's my tail. Would you like it with cream or chocolate?"

She stood up and walked over to him, and after putting her arms around him, she whispered, "Guess you were right, I will really wake up in the morning feeling like a different woman. When am I going to see you again?"

"Whenever you want," George replied.
"Call the Base, that's how you can get me, just ask for Driver 69, say you want to do some shopping."

She started to laugh again, and said, "Is that what they call it these days?"

George replied, smiling pointing down to his body, "You won't find this anywhere."

By the time George left Karen's house it was already two am.

At the door, he kissed her, and said, "You were amazing, write a list of all the things you would like to do, your deepest sexual fantasies and next time we will fulfil one, or maybe two." He kissed her again and said "Goodnight, sweet dreams."

Getting into his car he felt something in his back pocket, he reached in and found a chocolate after-eight and three hundred pounds; he smiled.

"Karen's List"

Three days later, Karen contacted the Base looking for George, saying she needed to be collected at eight pm. George parked his car again in the Dalkey Island Hotel and pressed the doorbell on the gate. Karen answered the intercom, "I'll buzz you in." The door was released, and he walked up to the front door of the house which was open. The house was even more incredible than he remembered, and Karen was coming down the stairs wearing a black dress, her hair no longer in a bun but flowing around her shoulders, her eyes accentuated by light touches of makeup, her lips red.

George looked at her and said "Wow, you're incredible."

Karen smiled and said, "You're too polite."

He met her as she reached the end of the stairs, their faces level, "I'm not being polite, you do look amazing." He reached out his hands and pulled her face to his as he kissed her, her tongue following his, he reached up her dress and felt her pussy hot and moist.

"You're horny, aren't you?" George looked into her eyes, smiling.

Karen replied, "I've been thinking of nothing else the last three days, I thought we might go for something to eat and then," before she could answer, George said, "Dessert."

George sat her on the third step and said, "Let me give you your appetiser first."

Karen feigned a protest, as George lifted her dress, revealing her black stockings. She was wearing tiny pink knickers, George pulled them to one side and started to lick her pussy. Karen tried to say, "No foreplay" but her mind was instantly distracted.

George opened her labia lips with his fingers and moving slowly he found her g-spot and then flipped his tongue like a fan across her open pussy, inserting two fingers deep inside her, touching a honeycomb of erotically charged nerve endings, his fingers deep inside her, they found her A-spot, his tongue and fingers working in tandem. Karen's whole body tightened as she released with a scream of ecstasy. George's head buried deep between her legs consuming her cum as her body twitched with each spasm. George licked her clean and pulled back her knickers.

Gently bringing her dress back down around her knees, he licked his lips and said, "Did you like your appetiser? I know I did."

Karen still trying to catch her breath, replied, "My whole body feels like jelly."

He smiled and kissed her passionately, he reached out his hand, she took it, he pulled her up from the stairs saying, "I think you will enjoy your dinner even better now."

Karen still smiling replied, "God, that was truly incredible, to think I thought oral sex was gross up to three days ago."

George asked her jokingly, "What happened three days ago?" she replied, "I met this artist, kind of good looking, with a humongous penis and a tongue like a snake."

George pulled her closer and said, "Only kind-of good looking," they both laughed.

Karen handed George the keys to her car and said, "Do you mind driving? you've made me a little distracted."

She took his hand and walked around to the back of the house where her Mercedes was parked.

George opened her door, Karen got in and said, "My, aren't you the gentleman, appetiser and chivalry, before we have dinner."

George replied, "Just wait until you see what I can do with a Banana."

"Surprise me," Karen responded laughing.

He got into the driver's door, sat in, leaned over, kissed her, and said, "You have so much to learn, now, where are we off to?"

"I've booked a table in the Grand Hotel in Wicklow for nine, we are going to be late because of," George interrupted her and said, "Foreplay," she laughed.

It was nine thirty by the time they were seated at a table and the waiter came over to George and asked if they would like drinks.

George replied, "The lady would like.."

Karen who was looking at the menu, looked up at him, surprised and said, "I will have a glass of Chardonnay please."

When the waiter left, she said, "You are extraordinarily chivalrous George, and do you know something? this is by far the best evening I have had in decades."

He looked at her smiling and taking her hand, he said, "It's only started my Xuesheng."

Karen asked him what that was, George replied, "It's Chinese for *student.*"

"I'm too old to be a student," she responded.

George gazed into her eyes and said, "Beauty only needs light to be seen. I hope to shine light on you and open your mind and body to everything you have been denied."

Karen looked at him quite seriously and said, "Why do you do this for work George? Sell yourself, maybe that's not the right word, you know what I mean."

George replied, looking straight at her, "I was asked to meet you by a friend, I never done this before, well I mean, I have never pimped myself. I said to my friend that If, I didn't find you attractive, it wouldn't go any further, but I did find you very attractive and it's cool just hooking up and having fun."

Smiling, Karen said, "I'm your first, you were a newbie."

George kissed her and asked her, "Did you write that list?"

Karen reached into her handbag and pulled out a cream envelope and handed it to him. "Here, this is the first list."

He laughed and said, "The first." He opened it, as Karen looked at his face, as he read it. When he finished, he put it down and said, "Nine things you fantasise about doing and one that you crave. Why do you want me to fuck your husband's girlfriend?"

Karen looked into George's eyes and said, "I want him to feel the humiliation and betrayal he made me feel, I want his heart shattered, I want him to feel like a fool."

"Why me?" George asked her.

She replied, "You're like one of those models off Vogue, you're bloody gorgeous looking and any woman would want to fuck you, even that one over there."

George looked over at a table with a couple, the girl in her late twenties smiled back at him.

Karen said, "She's been ogling you since you walked in, and her boyfriend is too thick to recognise it."

George replied, "Hell, there's no fury like a woman scorned, they say."

Karen responded. "This woman won't be made a fool off by a fucking little prick who came from nothing, a bloody parasite, feeding off my family's wealth, fucking some nurse who I paid to look after him while he recuperated from a horse-riding accident."

George interrupted her, and said, "How's the horse?"

Karen started to laugh, and said, "You must think I'm some kind of crazy woman."

He replied, "No Karen, I just think, you were hurt and are still in pain, and that's perfectly understandable. I will fuck her if that's what you want."

She looked up at him, wiping tears from her eyes and with such venom, said, "Yes, I want you to fuck her stupid. It will be the best ride she ever got, and I want to be there when he sees it."

George picked up the list and said with a big smile, "On a lighter note, you want to have sex in your car, would you like to find somewhere on the way back?"

Karen looked at him, and said, "Most definitely!"

An hour later, overlooking Bray Head, George parked her car, and switching off the lights, he pulled her over to him and kissed her. He slowly pulled down the lace straps off her shoulders along with the front of her dress. Her breasts popped out, her nipples dark and hard; he pushed her back into her seat, he leaned over and reclined it all the way back. Then, he climbed on top of her, his head bent beside the roof. Karen unbuttoned his jeans and took out his bulging cock, she opened her legs, and shouted, "Fuck me, just fuck me."

George pulled her dress up and pulled her knickers aside and forced his cock into her. She screamed, "Jesus, your fucking huge." He penetrated her deeper and with every thrust, Karen's legs hit off the window as she tried to open them wider, like a rag doll.

George spun her around; now she was on top of him, and he said, "Your turn."

He layback, looking at her tits bouncing as she rode him, he placed one hand on her pussy and started to stroke it with his other hand. He grabbed her ass and pulled her up and down, and just as he knew she was about to come, he stroked in-between her cheeks tipping her anus with his fingers. She orgasmed and collapsed onto him; he covered her with her dress and held her.

Karen sat up and said, "Wow, can't believe I just did that." Her tits still hanging outside her dress, George looked at her and said, "Sit on my face and let me suck you out." Karen didn't question, she just straddled his mouth as he sucked her cum, she turned around and saw he was pulling his cock.

"You're a horny bastard, aren't you?" she said.

"Now cum for me," George's hand wrapped around his cock, each stroke quicker than the last, she kept looking at him masturbating, "Pull your cock for me," Karen demanded.

George exploded like a missile.

She slid over into the driver's seat and said, "That's two of my ten marked off."

George looked over at her, and said, "Is it not just one? sex in a car."

Karen replied, "No, I wanted to dominate you."

George laughed and said, "That's not domination, my little Xuesheng, I will teach you how to manipulate every sexual fibre of my body, how to make my cock harder, how to stretch it, squeeze it, and torture my balls. Teach you every point in a man's body to turn him on."

Karen looked at him, and responded, "Jesus, I certainly am a virgin when it comes to sex." They both laughed.

When they got back to Karen's house she went to a safe in the wall of the sitting room and took out a file and handed it to George.

After reading it, George looked at her and said, "You really want to do this?"

Karen, even more unwavering, said, "I want him dead, but will accept his heart being ripped to pieces instead."

In that moment, George saw a side of her he didn't like, and his facial expressions was obviously betraying him as she walked over to him and said "If you're not comfortable doing it. It's okay."

George responded, "It's his loss, and if it was me, I would leave him to it, she's obviously a gold digger and he will see that eventually."

Karen kissed George's lips, and said, "I don't want to wait, I want him to suffer as I am."

George replied, "Okay, no worries, I will come up with a plan, now can we forget your ex and have some fun...?"

Karen's List. Gorgeous George and the File!

When Karen first suspected that her husband Frank was cheating on her, she engaged a private investigator called Marcus, whose work resulted in a detailed file containing pictures, dates, times, and all kinds of information regarding the other woman.

Her name was Leanne Kilbride, she was twenty-eight years old, a nurse working at Saint Luke's Hospital, where Karen's husband Frank was convalescing after his horse-riding accident.

By the time Marcus was employed, Frank had already established a routine, according to which, he met up with Leanne, two or three times a week, always in different locations; their secret *rendezvous* invariably ending at Leanne's flat where they had sex. Marcus was able to get some explicit pictures of Frank and Leanne through a downstairs window, which left nothing to the imagination and no possibility for Frank to deny it. Marcus also investigated Leanne; her date of birth, if she had any criminal background, and her work history, which proved that Frank wasn't the first patient Leanne had romantic relationships with. There were two previous patients, the last one resulted in Leanne leaving her former hospital and abruptly taking a lesser paid job. Marcus had also detailed Leanne's friends and movements, the make and model of her car, its registration, and the places where she socialised.

When George read the file, he learnt that Leanne went to Copper Face Jacks on Harcourt Street, a known hangout for nurses and Cops. The pictures also showed how much Leanne liked to party and enjoyed attention.

One picture showed her and her friends outside Coppers pissed drunk, hanging out of some doorman.

George found out that her birthday was two weeks away so he expected Leanne would be celebrating it at Coppers. So, he called the place pretending to be a strippergram service and using all his charm, he told the receptionist, Hannah, that he lost his appointment book.

Thanks to Hannah, he learnt that there were going to be eight girls attending the party and no guys. George smiled to himself. He knew that Leanne was in the honeymoon stage of her relationship.

His experience had taught him there were two types of women to avoid. One corresponded to Leanne's situation; the other was the loved up newly engaged woman. Not solely relying on his good looks, George planned Leanne's capture in great detail.

First of all, he needed a flash car, which he organised from his friend Terry who was a car sales rep for Mercedes in Ballybough.

Secondly, he needed an apartment near the city which was kindly provided by one of his married female friends Margery, who had one in Dame Street where she and George used it to fuck now and then.

In order to get her permission to use the flat, George contacted Margery, fucked her, and a day later called again saying that he must have dropped his credit card in her apartment. On that occasion, they met, and she gave him the key along with a big smile and the promise from him to keep it, until they met again.

Leanne's birthday party was scheduled for eight pm on a Saturday evening.

The night before, George parked outside Coppers, and talked to one of the doormen he knew from the gym George frequented, to whom he told that friends of his would be attending a party the next night and asked if he could give them the VIP treatment. Everything was organised.

Saturday morning, George contacted Saint Luke's Hospital, again in the role of a stripper-gram and asked Amy at the reception what time Leanne was finishing work so he could get her just as she was leaving work. Amy proved to be very helpful when she informed him that Leanne was on the early shift, so, she would be finishing at three, and would be out around three thirty.

Therefore, at three o' clock, George parked the brand-new red Mercedes Convertible he borrowed next to Leanne's Ford Fiesta. He got out and while pretending to be tying his shoelace, he stuck a banana up the exhaust pipe of her car.

Then, he went for a walk, and when he returned, twenty minutes later, he found Leanne intent on trying to start her car. He tapped her window and said, "Are you having car trouble?"

Leanne looked at him, her mouth open, "Yes, it's an old car, it's always playing up, can't believe it, it's my birthday, really needed it to work today."

George wished her happy birthday and offered to have a look at it. Taking off his jacket, he opened the door of the Merc and placed it on the seat.

Leanne staring at George's white shirt said, "It doesn't matter, I will get someone to get it sorted, you will get destroyed."

George insisted, and with the bonnet up, he pretended to play around with some leads, asking her to turn over the engine. She tried, but it didn't start, so, George closed down the bonnet, and said, "It will need a mechanic. I have a friend who owns a car company that will get it sorted for you. I will call him when I get back home."

Leanne noticed a big black oil stain on George's white cotton shirt. "I am so sorry you got your shirt ruined," she said, feigning her damsel in distress pose.

George asked her if she needed a lift and that he was heading to Blackrock, well aware that she lived with Frank in Sandymount, which also happened to be on the way.

Leanne refused twice but George insisted, particularly because it was her birthday. She got into his car.

George walked around the back of Leanne's Fiesta and quickly took out the banana and threw it away.

The moment he got in beside her, she said, "Is this brand new? It smells new."

George replied, "Didn't notice to be honest, I collected it yesterday, needed a run around."

Leanne just looked at him smiling, and said "This is a run around, wow."

George asked Leanne if she would mind if he dropped back to his apartment to change his shirt. George picked up his arm and looked at it. He deliberately scraped it under the bonnet along with the oil stain and pulled back his sleeve.

"Oh, did you do that off my car? I'm so sorry," Leanne responded.

George replied, "It's okay, I have a first aid kit in my apartment, I will sort it out."

George parked his car outside the apartment on Dame Street, he turned to Leanne and said, "Would you like a coffee or something while I change and sort this cut out?" Leanne not only agreed but offered to dress the wound, so, minutes later, she walked into the luxury apartment.

"Wow, this is amazing!" she couldn't help her response. George walked over to a press and took out a brand-new shirt he had placed earlier along with a First Aid kit. He asked Leanne if she minded if he took off his shirt. She jokingly replied she was a nurse and had seen plenty of guys naked. George took off his shirt revealing, his extremely athletic body and six-pack. He chose that moment to look at her eyes and saw her ogling him. He handed her the First Aid kit and he sat down, his muscular body next to hers.

"That's a gorgeous aftershave," Leanne said, trying to compose herself.

"Thank you, I got it in Belgium the other day, didn't know if I liked it or not."

Five minutes later, in her sweet nurse's voice, she said, "All done." George put on his shirt and threw his other shirt in the bin."

Leanne said, "You must let me pay for that."
George replied, "Not at all, the agency will pay for it."
Leanne asked him what he worked at.
George trying to be coy, said, "I hate telling people because they get the wrong impression, but I'm a model for Vogue."

Her eyes were still admiring him when she replied, "I had a feeling you were a model; I haven't seen a body like yours before and you are certainly a very attractive man."

George, again trying to be coy, replied, "That's the problem, women only see the surface, guess that's why I don't have a girlfriend."

Leanne replied immediately, "You don't have a girlfriend, you're kidding me."

George looked at his watch and said, "I'm so sorry, but I have to get to this meeting with a promoter." He looked at Leanne, and said, "Oh, I almost forgot," he walked over to the desk and picked up the phone and called the Base.

John answered, George, said, "Hello John, its George, could you sort out a car for a friend of mine, its parked in the grounds of Saint Luke's Hospital, the reg? Hold on."

George asked Leanne for the registration of her car. She couldn't remember it. George said to John, "it's a blue Ford Fiesta, that would be great, just bill the Agency."

Leanne tried to protest saying, he had done way too much. George responded with, "It's the Agencies money, to hell with them," they both laughed.

They headed down to the car, where George opened the door for her and she thanked him. Karen had told him, Frank wasn't at all chivalrous.

On the way, Leanne asked George if he was going out tonight, he replied, "Yes, I have another boring meeting with a client in Harcourt Street at nine."

Leanne replied, "God, that's amazing, I'm having a party in Coppers tonight, you should drop in."

George replied, "These meetings can go on forever, but if I get free, I will certainly drop in, and hopefully buy you a Birthday drink."

He dropped her off outside her apartment block on Serpentine Road in Sandymount, again promising to drop into her party.

By nine o' clock, Leanne's party was in full swing and, by then, she had already told her friends all about the gorgeous model driving the brand-new Mercedes with the fantastic body, her knight in shining armour.

Geraldine, her best friend, kept saying, "Are you sure you weren't dreaming girl?"

Just as the birthday cake arrived, a bottle of champagne was delivered to their table; Leanne looked at the waiter and said, "We didn't order that," and the waiter said, "It's with compliments from the guy over there."

They all turned around and looked at George who was waving over.

Geraldine, was the first to say something, "Oh my fucking God, he is fucking gorgeous."

Leanne waved at George to come over. He kissed each girl on the cheek while introducing himself with his usual smile and charm.

Then, speaking directly to Leanne he said, "I'm so sorry I can't stay but just wanted you to know my friend got your car sorted, and I wanted to wish you happy birthday."

The girls started to shout loudly, "You have to kiss the birthday girl, kiss her, kiss her."

George bent down smiling at Leanne and held her face gently in his big hands, his eyes fixed on her, as he brought her closer to his mouth and kissed her lips gently.

However, he soon felt her tongue trying to get into his mouth, so he wrapped his own around hers and swallowed deep before breaking the kiss.

Leanne was breathless. George reached out a card and said, "There's my number, give me a call sometime."

After that, he left to a rapture of screams and applause from the girls.

When they were queuing later for the nightclub, the main doorman called them out of the queue and said, "George asked me to look after you."
The girls kept telling Leanne she would be mad not to call him. Geraldine kept saying the whole night, "Forget calling him, I would give my kidneys to fuck him, he's gorgeous and fucking rich for God's sake. Dump that awl fella you're with."

Four days later, Leanne rang the number George had given her. It was the fax line that John switched over to use as his private number.

John answered, "Hello?" Leanne asked, if she could speak to George. John replied, this was his answering service and told her if she left a number, George would get back to her. Leanne left the number of Saint Luke's and asked George to call her.

Immediately, George got in touch with Karen and told her that he had Leanne hooked. Karen didn't even know anything about George's plan but was extremely happy to hear Leanne wanted to meet George. He told Karen that if everything went to plan, he would get her back to a bedroom in Wynn's Hotel, but before he would make sure to leave word at the reception desk for her and leave the bedroom door unlocked.

George called Leanne at work; she wanted to thank him for everything he had done, and she told him, the car started straight away.

George interrupted her, and said, "Would you like to meet for dinner?"

Leanne paused and said, "Not tonight but maybe tomorrow night, is that okay?"

George replied, "That's perfect, do you want to meet in Wynn's Hotel, at let's say, eight?"

Leanne replied, "Yes."

George updated Karen by stating, "it's on."

He informed her on what time dinner was booked for and he considered that by ten, he would be fucking her.

Exactly at eight o clock Leanne walked into the reception of Wynn's Hotel.

George walked in behind her, kissed her, and said, "You look fantastic, so hope you're hungry."

Leanne smiled and said, "Yes, I'm starving."

George was extremely tentative to her, pouring her wine as he flirted with her for an hour, occasionally bending over close to her face, whispering he wanted to kiss her.

After the third glass of wine, Leanne put her arms around his face, pulled him in, and French kissed him. Any restraint she held, suddenly left her body as her tongue probed his mouth and her hands travelled down his chest. George knew she wanted him, more and more, they flirted until George said, "Would you like to come up to my room?"

Leanne replied, "You have a room here?"

He replied, "The agency has one all the time."

He kissed her again, she said, "What about your apartment?"

George replied, "It's set up for a photo shoot tomorrow."

She kissed him and said, "Okay, let me just go to the loo first."

George went to the reception desk to leave a note he had already written for Karen. He handed the receptionist a piece of paper and asked her, if she could call that number and say, "The shoot is on."

It was Karen's week to have the children, so, she came up with a perfect plan to get Frank into the hotel.

As soon as the receptionist called her house, Karen gave Frank a ring, telling him, at nine forty-five, that Olivia, their daughter, was in trouble in town, and that he had to meet her as soon as possible outside the Wynn's Hotel.

Meanwhile, back in the hotel room, George was slowly undressing Leanne, kissing her neck, and rubbing his fingers across her tits. Leanne was like an adolescent teenager, extremely impatient, while unzipping her dress and taking off her bra. She just wanted to get fucked.

George looked at her and said, "We have all the time in the world."

She lunged at George's jeans, opening them with such experience he didn't feel the buttons open. She pulled down his pants, and his cock stood out. "Jesus," she said, "You are bloody perfect in every way."

Once again, George tried to slow her down, she was like a dog in heat, it was like she hadn't had sex in years. He lay her down on her back, on the bed, she already had her legs open and, as he went down on her, she grabbed his head, shoving it deeper into her pussy, screaming, "Oh fuck yes, God yes."

George knew he needed to prolong her climax; he knew she was a one hit wonder. As soon as she came, he knew she would want to be dressed and gone, so he played with her pussy, and every time her thighs tightened, he would change rhythm, stopping her deliberately from orgasming.

Karen went straight into the reception of Wynn's Hotel and asked for a note addressed to her, which the receptionist handed to her. It said, "I'm in room 635, make a noise so I can arrange a great picture."

Karen went back outside and waited for Frank. He arrived ten minutes later all flustered, asking her what's going on. Karen said Olivia was with some guy in room 635, and that he was hurting her. Immediately, Frank ran into the hotel, passed the reception desk, and turned the corner to the left. He pressed the elevator button instinctually. Karen realised Frank knew the layout of the hotel very well. He pressed the button for floor six, the doors closed; again, Karen thought to herself, "How did he know, to press six?"

As the lift door opened, Karen could see Marcus down the corridor outside room 635 as she had arranged. Karen deliberately kicked over a steel bin making one hell of a racket, and said, in a loud voice. "Oh, I am so sorry." George heard the noise and told Leanne to straddle his cock and fuck him. Like a cowgirl in a rodeo, she climbed onto him and fucked him, just as Frank ran into the room, he could hear a girl screaming, "Fuck me, fuck me, yes, yes."

He got closer to the bed and finally realised it wasn't Olivia but his Leanne.

On the other hand, Marcus was busy snapping pictures, the flash lighting up the room every second.

Leanne started screaming, "Get the fuck out."

That's when George stood up; his bulging cock still erect. Frank looked at George's erect cock as he passed him, like a Peacock. George walked into the bathroom, Frank, now realising what was going on, shouted at Karen, "You fucking bitch, you organised this."

George returned with his jeans on and began picking up the rest of his clothes.

Then, he went over to Leanne, who was sitting up in the bed with the bed covers around her, still screaming for everyone to get out, and after taking a fifty-pound note from his jeans he threw it at Leanne's face, saying, "I'm not fucking you for fifty quid with all of these here that's not what we agreed. Is this your old guy, who doesn't give you head or a good ride? I can see why, you needed to pay me."

George looked down his nose at Frank as he passed him and left the room. Karen followed him; Marcus was already at the elevator, they all got in, George still getting dressed, they all laughed. Karen was the first to speak, "Ok, that was unreal." Marcus said, "Have some good photos."

George looked at Marcus and said, my face must be hidden, okay?"

Marcus replied, "I could give you a job today son, you are certainly well endowed." Marcus, guaranteed, "I will blank out your face."

Marcus promised Karen he would talk to her in the morning and when they got down to reception, he left.

George looked at Karen and said, "I need to shower and get her stench off my skin."

But Karen still high on adrenaline, didn't hear a word of what George had just said. So, George asked Karen if she heard him, and she looked at him and said, "Thank you, I owe you." He walked her to the car and tried to kiss her, but she turned her head and said, "Shower that bitch off you, I will call you later."

"Driver 6, Poor Peter, Gets Snared"

It might be hard to imagine a world where mobile phones didn't exist, forced to go to a telephone box to call someone. Nevertheless, in the eighties and even nineties, that was the way in which the world operated.

Originally, the kids from the inner city had a trick they called *snaring*, which was used to catch birds; but later, they modified it, to make it, more financially rewarding. Simple, but extremely effective, the trick consisted in finding a telephone box that was working and hammer a six-inch nail into the door, being careful in leaving just the head of the nail on the other side.

Then, once someone got in, and had their back turned, they would run up, and whack the nail all the way in, so that the caller would find himself locked in the box.

John called Peter, "Driver 6, have the ball and strife on here, can you give her a call?"

Peter was just leaving the city empty and saw a telephone box just outside the Bingo Hall on the North Strand and parked his taxi beside it. He opened the door of the telephone box, stepped in, and he was about to pick up the receiver when he jumped because of the sound of a loud bang. The phone box shook. He turned to see three little *gurriers* aged between ten and thirteen laughing. The one with a lump hammer in his hand turned to his friend and said, "Damo, we got ourselves another fuckn numbnut."

Peter, still shaken, tried to open the door pushing it hard but it wouldn't budge.

So, he asked the kids to open the door, but they only started laughing even harder.

"What's it worth to yea?" Damo said, and Peter trying to humour the kids answered, "I will give you fifty pence each."

They all laughed again. "Fucking fifty pence, what are you like?"

Peter was getting panicked in the box and started to bang on the glass, shouting, "Let me out!"

The kids now were surrounding the box, looking in at Peter, and banged back on the glass screaming, "Give us your fucking wallet!"

One of them walked over to Peter's car and tried to open the doors. The driver's door opened. Peter started to shout at them that he would ring the Guards.

Damo replied, "And how are you going to do that Numbnut? the phone is not working."

Peter picked up the receiver, there was no dial tone. He turned and seen the three gurriers in his car ransacking it. Damo came back over to the phone box and said, "Give us the fuckn keys to yar car Numbnut or else."

Peter got brave and said, "Or else what?"

Damo, in response, took out a rat from the nearest bin, and walked behind the phone box; seconds later, the rat was in beside Peter, who was now screaming, "Get it out, get it out!" Peter's feet prised against the glass, in order to keep his body up off the floor, while outside the gurriers kept laughing and imitating Peter's screams. "Get it out, get it out."

After that, Damo asked the others if they had hotwired the car yet and while Peter continued to frantically push the door open, Damo said to him, "Hey mister, me rat will eat yer bollox, he's fucking starving like Marvin."

Peter shouted at him, "You're going to prison. This is called kidnapping."

The kids couldn't respond for how much they were laughing, but eventually Damo said, "How could we be kidnapping your arse when you're an owl fuckn geezer? would you Cop on to yer self, numbnut."

A Cop car was passing; one of the kids noticed it and called the others who all ran off towards the flats.

Despite Peter's frantically waving to the Cops, they passed him by without noticing him.

While still holding himself up off the ground with the rat running under his feet, Peter resigned himself to wait for a passer-by.

Eventually, an old woman arrived; Peter banged the glass at her, scaring the woman almost to death. He asked her, to get help. He couldn't get out. But the woman simply replied, "You're off, your head, and you can't get out of a phone box, those are some bad drugs your taken mister," and she kept walking.

Twenty minutes, later a couple passed through; Peter called them, told them that kids had nailed the door shut, and asked for help. However, the male said, he didn't want to get involved and that Coronation Street was just about to start. His girlfriend instead, asked Peter if he would make it worth their while. Peter promised them five pounds if they got help.

They asked Peter to pass them the money through a hole in the glass placed on the top of the box.

Peter complied, but the moment the male took the fiver he said, "Fuckn sweet what a dify!" and taking his girlfriend by the arm, the two left laughing.

Another twenty minutes passed until another couple approached. Peter again told them the story; this time promising to give them five pounds if they managed to get him out.

They disappeared and returned five minutes later just as two fire engines arrived, red lights flashing. One of the fire crew called for a crowbar, and within a minute the nail was pulled out.

As soon as the door opened the rat ran up towards the flats in the same direction of the kids. Peter, on the other hand, stood out soaked in sweat from holding himself up. The fireman asked him if he needed an ambulance, but he refused, thanked them, and was just about to get into his car when he noticed that one of the kids had wiped his arse on the seat. Peter reached over and grabbed his mic, but it came off in his hand. The kids were guilty of cutting it, in the same way in which they were responsible for drawing a big moustache on his identification picture. Peter tried to clean the seat, but eventually he decided to take a floor mat and placed it over the skid mark.

Even with every window down, the smell was still overwhelming as Peter drove to the closest Petrol station to clean his car.

Driver 60, Keith, Aka "Seeds"

It might be impossible to perceive a world without YouTube, Twitter, mobile phones, Facebook, or even the internet. Therefore, it might be also difficult to try to envisage a world where sperm donors were considered part of science fiction.

During the eighties, if you were a single female, or gay, and wanted a child in Catholic Ireland, you were called an abomination or harlot from the alters of every church in Ireland.

Keith was a thirty-three-year-old taxi man, and a father of six children. Physically, his children could have been poster kids as they all had angelic faces, big blue eyes, and mops of curly blonde hair. Hence, he would proudly display their picture on the dashboard of his taxi, and that is how he became to be known as "Seeds."

JJ Smiths in Angier Street held a function for lesbians every Sunday night and around the corner there was, *Incognito*, a club for gay men and women, all of which were illegal and considered morally disgusting by the pillars of society. Such was the irony; the same pillars of society frequented the same clubs of the so-called *dregs*.

Still, Keith didn't care about people's sexual orientation, or the colour of their skin particularly because every time he parked outside gay clubs he could get three fares, instead of just one from a straight club at the same time slot.

One night, he picked-up a couple outside JJ's, and after getting in the backseat they immediately started talking about his children, how beautiful they were, they steered the conversation to how desperately they wanted a child,

137

but were unlucky in their search for a guy willing to play his part. The two were waiting for his response, but he didn't say anything, so, they introduced themselves as Laura and Catherine. They both appeared quite masculine, Laura so much more than her partner, that, for Keith it was obvious who played the dominant role in the relationship.

They didn't tell Keith that they had travelled with him before, had checked him out, knew where he lived, or that Catherine was ovulating. They had simply planned to seduce him.

All of a sudden, Laura asked him if he was happily married. Keith replied he was.

Laura looked at Catherine who couldn't hide her disappointment, and Laura, raising her hand to her, silently mouthed, "It's okay." Then, she asked Keith if he had ever thought about selling his sperm.

"Not something that ever crossed my mind," he replied.

The rest of the conversation was mundane until he parked outside their house. Blatantly, Laura asked Keith if he would like to fuck both of them because they wanted to have kids and he certainly was making beautiful babies. Keith replied he was flattered, but he had already enough problems.

It was now clear for Catherine that Laura was getting physically annoyed, as she silently mouthed to her, "We are a problem, Prick?" She took his rejection as an insult to her womanhood so, Catherine placed her arm on Laura's leg.

But Laura suddenly sat up, came in between Keith's seat, and biting her tongue she said, "I will give you two hundred quid to fuck Catherine." She looked back at Catherine, who was mortified, "No messing, just straight in and cum. Two minutes for two hundred quid."

In spite of the fact that Keith's taxi insurance was up the following week, and he badly needed the money, he said, "No." Laura paid him, and while she was getting out, she said, "I tried it the easy way."

Six weeks later, Keith was driving down Clanbrassil Street, and a Cop car came up behind him signalling him, to pull over. A female Cop got out and walked up to his window and asked him to step out of the vehicle so that she could search his car.

In her uniform he didn't recognise her, but it was Laura. Taking out a small plastic bag of white powder from under his seat, she asked him "What's this?" Keith said, "That's not mine."

She laughed and beckoned her fellow officer to come over. He got out and said, "What do we have here? looks like heroin to me," he replied.

"Says it's not his," Laura said.

"Sure, they all say that" was the male Cops answer, as he walked back to the patrol car and got in.

At the same time, she went back to Keith and said, "Remember me?" He looked at her but still couldn't remember; that really infuriated Laura. "You thought you were too good to fuck my girlfriend, remember me now?"

Keith looked at her again and nodded as the blood left his face.

"I'm going to do you under the misuse of Drugs Act of 1977." She came right up to his face, and said, "You are going to lose your taxi licence and probably your home."

Keith, now crying, begged her not to do it. He said, he would do anything, he would fuck anyone whenever she wanted. Laura told him her colleague had witnessed the drugs so if he messed her about, she would have him arrested.

Reminding him of the address, she told him to show up at her place the next night at eight. If he wasn't there, she would get a warrant for his arrest, and if he told anyone, she assured him, nobody would believe the word of a junky taxi man over that of a police officer.

The next night Keith knocked on Laura's door; she opened it, and said, "Up the stairs."

He walked up to find Catherine smiling and saying, "Hello." She obviously didn't know what Laura was doing or how she was blackmailing him to fuck her.

Once in the bedroom, Laura walked over to a drawer, took out a bundle of cash, peeled off two hundred pounds, handed it to Keith, and said, "Okay, get your cock out and get it hard, start wanking yourself, I want you ready to cum." She looked at him menacingly, bending down to him as he was taking off his jeans and whispered, "Don't say a word."

Catherine said to him, "I'm just lifting my skirt, I don't want you feeling me or anything, just cum as quickly as you can." She stood up and stepped out of her knickers.

Laura went in-between Catherine's legs and started licking and fingering her pussy. She turned around to see Keith, who was standing and pulling his cock. She stood up and as he got in between Catherine's legs, she told him, "There's a good boy, she's nice and wet for you."

His cock had no problem finding her pussy; he pushed it into her and started to fuck her.

140

Behind his back, Laura took out a camera and pictured him; then, putting the camera away she moved her hand between his legs and started to play with his balls.

He came almost immediately. Laura squeezed his balls, saying, "Let's get every drop."

Finally, she tapped his naked ass, she laughed, and said, "There's a good little boy, that wasn't so hard."

He got up off Catherine, pulled up his jeans and said goodbye to Catherine. While walking him down the stairs Laura said to him, "You will come here every month until she gets pregnant, got it?"

Keith tried to say something, but she grabbed him, pushed him against the wall and said, "Who the fuck do you think you are, scumbag taxi man, you're my fucking bitch or you will be some prisoner's bitch."

Keith didn't hear anything until six weeks later.

Laura called the Base and asked for Keith to give Laura from Kimage a call. John would never call a driver to say a woman was looking for him, in case a member of his family was in the car. He always got the driver to ring the Base, using some excuse.

Keith called John five minutes after starting. John delivered the message.

In the previous weeks, Keith had tried to blank what had happened. He was riddled with guilt and hadn't told anything to Amy, his wife, who kept asking him what was wrong with him since the night he fucked Catherine. He knew his own wife wouldn't believe him and that nobody else would either. So, he ignored the call.

The next day, Laura called again with the same message. John told him he better call her in case she turned psycho. He dialed the number and Laura answered.

Keith said, "Hello, this is.." but, before he finished Laura interrupted him and said, "Daddy."

Laura laughed and said, "You certainly have great seed. Catherine's pregnant and you're going to be a daddy."

Keith didn't hear much after that as he slumped down into the phone box.

He rang back an hour later, asking what she wanted. Laura told him they didn't want anything from him, just that Catherine wanted him to know.

For months after Keith lived in a state of fear, not sleeping, thinking that they would knock on his door.

Eventually, he blanked it out like it never happened and resumed normal life, until Laura called again.

Gorgeous George and the Cop's Wife

Like most of George's romantic liaisons he never got the time to find out much about the women he was sleeping with, that usually came after the event or mostly not at all. This was particularly true for a woman he picked up outside the Bleeding Horse Pub in Camden Street one Saturday night. Getting into the back of his car, she asked him to take her to Stillorgan Wood. George looked at her in his rear-view mirror.

She was in her early thirties, black shoulder length hair, beautiful brown eyes, and with red lipstick that was always a turn-on for him. He noticed her looking at his taxi identification picture and then to his face.

"I thought that was a picture of some male model you put up as a joke," she said.

George turned around in his seat, looked at her smiling and replied, "Nope, that's me".

"I can see that," she said with a big smile, "guess you must be asked that all the time."

Again, he turned around and replied, "Yes."

"If you don't mind me asking, why is someone like you driving a taxi?" she asked.

George had lots of personas he used, from freelancing in a modelling agency, to being an artist, or a student of acting; for her, he was going to be an artist.

"I do this between assignments, I absolutely love art."

Looking at her again through his mirror, he understood from her facial expression that she was intrigued.

"What type of art?" she asked.

"Sculpture mainly, I like working with my hands, I love the way wet clay feels taking hours to form and mould, revealing the beauty I can see that's there," he replied. Again, watching her response to his words, he could see her smirking. Then, she came forward in her seat, her face almost beside his, so that he could smell her perfume, and she asked him if he could stop at a shop on the way.

Five minutes later, he stopped in Donnybrook, outside a late-night shop. She asked him as she was getting out if he wanted anything. He replied, he was fine. When she returned, she opened his front passenger door and got in beside him.

In that moment, he realised she was more than intrigued. Through her coat, now open, he could see she had a fantastic body, and two amazing legs that were being revealed through a slit in her dress that seemed to go all the way up.

She caught his eyes looking at her, "You could be a model yourself," he said, trying to deflect from his glare.

Smiling, she reached out her hand and said, "I'm Nicole, what's your name?"

He turned and looked right into her eyes and replied "George." He noticed she was wearing a wedding ring on her finger. "Are you still married?" he asked her.

She replied, "Not if you don't want me to be."

At the next red traffic light junction he stopped, he reached out his right hand and brought her face to his and kissed her; her tongue cold as it explored his mouth like a snake. The car behind beeped his horn, so George broke from the kiss and saw that the traffic lights were green.

"Guess you're not married then," he said, smiling at her.

She responded, laughing "Guess I'm not."

Then, she took his left hand off the gear leaver and placed it on her leg.

She smiled at him, and said, "Show me how good you are with your hands." She reclined her seat and he started to caress her, moving his fingers slowly in a circular motion behind her knee, feather touching her inner thighs. He could feel the heat from her pussy before his fingers reached it, so, he proceeded to squeeze her thigh, opened her legs wider, and after placing his hand over her knickers, he could feel she was already hot and moist under his fingertips. She sighed as he slid his fingers under her knickers, rubbing her lips; he flipped two fingers back and forth across them, slowly massaging them apart, inserting one finger into her.

Nicole's moans were getting louder; he turned off from the main dual carriageway and onto a side road that was dimly lit and stopped the car. Still playing with her, he unclipped his safety belt and bent down until his head was between her legs. With his face only inches away from her pussy, he could now smell and taste her desire. He pulled her knickers to the side to allow his tongue to taste and tease her, and she started to moan harder right away, opening her legs instinctually for his head to get deeper. As his tongue explored her, her thighs started to tighten around his head. He knew she was about to cum, so he changed rhythm, and moving up, he kissed her mouth, while his fingers returned to her pussy.

She screamed, "I need to fuck you so bad!"

George asked her if she wanted to go somewhere more remote. She replied that her house was empty because her husband was working nights and wouldn't be back until seven in the morning.

Five minutes later, George turned into Stillorgan Wood. Nicole instructed him to drop her off outside her house, and to park his car at the start of the Estate. George knew by that instruction this wasn't her first rodeo.

After parking his taxi, he walked up to the front door of her house, she opened it, and instantly grabbed George, and pulled at his jeans. Her hand went down them to feel his cock "Fucking hell, that's big, haven't seen one that big before," she said, smiling. She grabbed it and started to twist it, her mouth sucking it as her fingers played with his balls.

Then, she came up and kissed him. He pushed her up against the wall, kissing her as he reached in-between her legs and pulled her knickers down. Bending down again, he mouthed her pussy, she grabbed his head, pushing it deeper, grinding her pussy off his face.

"Give me that cock!" she screamed. He stood up and penetrated her, her arms tightened around his shoulder with the force of his cock pushing inside her. "Fuck me, fuck me!" she screamed.

So, he turned her around; her face was now pressed against the wall as he lifted her dress, opened the cheeks of her ass, pushed his cock between them into her pussy, and started fucking her from behind. Her body was banging against the wall with every thrust, his fingers between her legs teasing her. George kept pumping her and fingering her.

Every time she was about to cum, he stopped her, which he could feel was driving her mad. She pushed him onto the floor, saying, "Jesus, I need this." Straddling him, she started to ride his cock, like she hadn't had sex in years, her body releasing her cum over his balls. Her

146

smell drove him deeper inside her and, as he brought his body to her face, kissing her, he reached around her dress and unzipped it, and pulled it over her head so her tits could bounce down.

As he lay on the floor, he reached up to cup her tits with his hand, and to continue playing with her nipples. He could read the desperation across her face, disguised as a smile as he kept stroking her pussy, until she came with a scream and slumped down onto his chest.

George looked at her smiling and said, "Guess you needed that."

Nicole replied, "You have no idea."

George didn't ask what she meant, he knew from so many married women he slept with, how selfish men could be, where foreplay was considered just a grope, and sexual satisfaction would be found later as they resorted to pleasuring themselves beside a sleeping husband.

He looked at her and said, "I have a question for you, what did you buy in the shop?"

She smiled and said, "Nothing, I wanted you, and I didn't want to make it look obvious," she laughed and kissed him and asked, "Do you like doing it in the shower?"

He grabbed her and said, "I like doing it anywhere."

"Let's have one!" Nicole said, as she stood up naked and walked up the stairs. George looked at her cute ass, picked up his clothes and followed her. Upstairs, she pointed to the bedroom; he walked in and stripped off, placing his clothes on a seat beside the bed.

Then, he went into the bathroom where Nicole had the shower running. She grabbed his cock as he entered the room, "Give me that," she said, laughing and pulling him by his cock.

The front door closed.

Nicole looked at George with fear etched across her face, "Fuck, it's my husband!" she said.

George replied, "I thought he wouldn't be back until seven. Can you get my clothes from your bedroom?" George asked her.

Nicole's husband called up to her, "Was my little princess drunk tonight? I can see your dress on the floor in the sitting room. Mrs Fleming must be shagging a taxi man again. I've seen a taxi parked outside her house as I came in, she has no shame."

George ran into the back bedroom. With his heart racing he saw, through the gap in the door a tall guy coming up the stairs and wearing a Garda uniform. George cursed himself, "Fuck, for fuck sake, a Cop's wife! What was I thinking?" He looked around the room for something to wear.

In the meantime, Nicole walked out of the shower and still naked met her husband at the bathroom door and said, "What are you doing home, Steven?"

He replied, "Wow, I must come home unexpected more often, we got a call in the area, so I thought I would drop in and see my little princess."

"Is the patrol car outside?" she asked him.

"Yes, but don't worry I can play truant, will bring it back at six."

Nicole kissed him and said, "Go in, wash your little mister, and follow me into the bedroom. I will give you something nice."

Two minutes later, George could hear him fucking her, coming straight away, apologising, and Nicole telling him it was alright.

George took the sheet off the bed and wrapped it around his waist, opened the window and climbed out onto the ledge. He closed the window gently behind him, the roof tiles of the kitchen extension were just under his feet, so he walked along them trying not to make a noise. When he got to the corner, he jumped onto the boundary wall and dropped down the other side and into the wooded area behind the houses.

He tried to avoid nettles and stingers but in the pitch dark was nearly impossible, so he kept getting stung and scraped every time he moved. Eventually, he found a well walked path and navigated his way around the back of the houses to his car.

However, when he got to it, he realised the keys to his car where in his jeans. So, George had to pick up a stick, broke it so as to leave a sharp end, and pushed it into the rubber that held the glass in the back passenger window in order to detach it.

Fortunately, the glass fell onto his hand, and he was able to reach in, open the door and sat into the back seat.

Once inside, George picked up the radio and called in, "John don't reply, I need help around Stillorgan Wood, I'm buck naked in the back of my car, after fucking a Cop's wife, lucky escape, my clothes and keys are in hers."

John called out, "Anyone around Stillorgan, Driver 69 having car trouble."

Buckets, founding himself around Stillorgan was the first to ring the Base, and after being updated he drove behind George's car. George got out in his sheet wearing it like a toga and jumped into Buckets taxi.

"I'm fucking freezing," George said the moment he sat in. "Can you turn up the heating?"

Buckets looked at him and said, "What the fuck happened to you?" looking at his arms, shoulders, and legs full of cuts, he said, "You're some dozy cunt fucking a Cop's wife."

"I didn't know," George replied.

Buckets responded, "Young, dumb, and full of cum, now what's the story here?"

George told him that his keys were in his jeans in the bedroom; he didn't care about his clothes but needed his keys. It had his apartment key on it. Buckets told him to go back to his car and that he would be back in a few minutes.

Buckets drove down to the number George told him; he could see the Garda car outside. Buckets got out, opened the bonnet of his car, took a bottle of water, and poured some on the hot exhaust manifold, so that steam started to pour from under the lid.

Afterwards, he went up to the front door and knocked. Steven opened the door wearing a bathrobe. Buckets immediately apologised for disturbing him, informing him that his car had just broken down and he needed water for the radiator.

Steven looked out at Bucket's car and saw the steam still flowing.

Buckets said, "A kettle of water will get me home Sir."

Steven said, "No problem. Stay there, and I will get you some," he walked into the kitchen.

150

Buckets after seeing Nicole at the top of the stairs, started simulating someone intent on putting a key into an ignition and turning it, then putting on clothes.

She understood and gave him the thumbs up.

Steven came back with a kettle.

Buckets took it and went down to his car, poured it over the exhaust again, and another raft of smoke appeared. So, he went back up to the door and said, "Could I possibly trouble you for another one Sir, I'm so sorry."

Steven, now annoyed, said, "Okay."

He took the kettle and went back into the kitchen.

Taking advantage from his husband's absence, Nicole appeared with a filled pillowcase and handed it to Buckets. After that, she quickly ran back up the stairs.

Buckets, on the other hand, went down to his car and put it on the driver's seat, then, he returned with his wallet, and while opening it, he said to Steven, who was waiting with another kettle, "Take this Sir, you have been so helpful," and handed him a ten-pound note.

Steven politely refused his generosity and handed him another kettle.

Again, Buckets went down, pretended to fill his car, and returned the kettle thanking Steven.

When Buckets drove back to George and gave him the pillowcase, warned him to stay away from her, "That's serious trouble you don't want!"

Driver 34, Geoffrey, Aka, "Jesus."

Piss-soakers, the name, is self-explanatory. Ever wonder why, there was a rug over the back seat of a taxi? Most Taxi Drivers couldn't afford to lose a weekend night, and Piss-soakers, usually happened at the weekends.

Male passengers had a tendency to tell a Taxi Driver when they needed to pee. Regrettably, either through embarrassment, or the fact that a strange man was driving them home, or for whatever other reason, female passengers didn't ask.

After a night out drinking, within minutes of the motion of the car, they needed to go to the toilet; sometimes they would end up using the seat as a toilet; a fact that was never detected until the next passenger sat in.

That's why experienced Taxi Drivers always had newspapers, one or two magic trees, and a fresh blanket to cover the mess. The next passenger to travel would act like a sponge pressing down on the blanket and papers soaking up the piss, and that's the reason why they were called "Piss-soakers."

"Jizzers," were masturbator's who would wackoff in the back of a taxi. Some found it perverse or even funny; to rub the Taxi Driver's shoulder with their open hand covered in Jizz, on the way out.

Yet, there was no difference between the sexes when it came to "shartters." A *shart*, is a cross between a shite and a fart. When holding wind, passengers often shit their pants, when they farted. Nothing worse, than sitting in a confined space when a person shits themselves.

Vomit heads were an occupational hazard. You learned the obvious signs quickly. Car window going down for them to get some air, flopping head, and whiteness of the face. Again, most were women, guys would ask a Taxi Driver to pull over, women, would try to hold it, and then like a projectile, it would cover a taxi, in wall, to wall, vomit, usually over the Taxi Drivers hair and down his neck. Silage charge being only twenty pounds, didn't cover the loss of Taxi Driver's earnings.

The worst part was however, having to clean another human beings' bodily fluids. The smell of excrement, semen, or vomit took days to leave the car; that would explain the over population of magic trees in taxis.

Geoffrey was a fifty-two-year-old reformed alcoholic who found Christ joining the Reborn Christian Society. Affectionately called, "Jesus" by his co-workers because of the rosary beads, hanging from his rear-view mirror. He gave passengers cards of the immaculate heart, blessing them with holy water while trying to convert them to Christ. He detested profanity, and was always reporting, John, the Base Controller, Buckets of Blood and Nuts, to management. Trading-in his old, bent up, Hillman Avenger, for a new, Datsun, Laurel.

After fourteen years, he decided to invest in a new car, which had all the mod cons, electric sunroof, electric windows, centralised locking, and a CD system.

Geoffrey was driving it off the forecourt when he stopped and went back, to retrieve his Holy Mary, as he called it. A four-inch, plastic statue that he placed in the middle of his dashboard for good luck.

In the eighties, it wasn't unusual for groups of English girls to come over to Dublin for Hens weekends.

154

Boisterous, promiscuous, sometimes aggressive, they all drank like sailors. They were great fun to bring into town, but the very ones to avoid later.

Showing their tits or pulling up their skirts, they always wanted to stop to get a kebab or a curry that inevitably stank out a taxi, and if they didn't puke, the next passenger surely did because of the smell.

Geoffrey broke one of the golden rules of Taxi-ing when he picked up four hens at three am on a Sunday Morning. One sat beside Geoffrey, while the others sat in the back. The girl beside him, said that they wanted to go to the Monte Clare Hotel, just off Merrion Square, which was less than a five-minute drive.

"Driver 34, away, to the Square, with four beautiful ladies", Geoffrey blew into John.

"Lucky man 34, being able to pick up four ladies, I can't pick one up," John replied.

All the girls laughed and Geoffrey assuming the role of the good Christian, asked them, "Are you going to mass in the morning girls?"

One of the drunken girls in the back replied, "Am I going to masturbate in the morning? You dirty fucker!" They all laughed, apart from Geoffrey, who was disgusted.

"May God forgive you. I asked you if you would be attending Mass in the morning," Geoffrey replied.

The same, mouthy-one in the back replied, "If God, can see every woman and man I've fucked, I'm certainly going to fucking hell. Are you one of those Joevo witnesses or something?"

Geoffrey, now blessing himself said, "I have God in my heart."

"I'd prefer to have, a tongue, in me pussy," the mouthy one responded, again, causing all her friends to laugh.

Looking through his rear-view mirror, he could see she had just started to kiss the girl beside her. Grabbing his bottle of holy water, he doused it over them, blessing them, "I will say a prayer for your souls."

"Fuckoff, pervo, don't need your fucking prayers, or your voodoo water. Now just, shut the fuck up, and drive," the mouthy-one aggressively replied.

Geoffrey, shocked and startled, timidly responded, "There is no need for such profanity."

Her friend, next to them, who, up to that point, was semi unconscious, even drunker than the rest of them, kept saying, "who's yer one?" She kept repeating it, over, and over, "Who's, yer one?"

Eventually, her girlfriend asked her, "Who are you talking about Sylvia?" she pointed her finger out the front window of the car, "Yer one."

Her friend looked and said, "there's nobody there."

Annoyed, Sylvia grabbed her friends head, and brought it down to hers, and pointed again, "Look, can you see her now, she's on the bonnet."

Realising she was pointing at the statue of Mary, the girls started to laugh so hard, that the one behind Geoffrey's seat, released a projectile vomit, which completely showered him.

Still laughing, she also had a shart, and with the smell of vomit and shite, one of the other two ended up puking in the back and over her friend.

Geoffrey keyed his mic and blew in a Charlie; the vomit still dripping off his bald head.

John replied, "What's the problem Driver 34?"

156

"I'm covered in vomit, and this disgusting human being beside me, has shitted on my seat. And the others, in the back, who were snogging, each other, puked as well."

John repeated it, in his particular fashion, "Okay, Driver 34, you have two girls in the back of your car snogging. Something is now dripping off your head, and the girl beside you, has filled her knickers. Is that right, Driver 34? Anyone, around, to give Driver 34 a hand?" the endless jibes and comments flowed.

"The Duce, won't give him a hand."

"Does he want a shovel to dig out, her knickers?"

"Greedy fucker taking on four."

"Those rosary beads would frighten the shit out of anyone."

John trying not to laugh, asked Driver 34. if he needed the police, which started more comments.

"For fuck sake, it's going to be an orgy."

Nuts was the first to arrive on the scene; the four girls were now standing by the wall of the hotel. Walking over to Geoffrey's car, he opened the passenger door, and the smell of shite and vomit filled his lungs.

Nuts went into character and managed to perfectly imitate the commentary of the six-million-dollar man, TV series, of course adapting it to the situation.

"She's shitting up chief, she can't hold it. She's better than she was before, squitter, runnier, blastier."

Then, Nuts did a slow-motion of himself, running like Lee Majors, going over to Geoffrey. Nuts placed his arm around him and said, in Humphrey Bogart voice, "It's a shitty job, kid!"

Geoffrey, looked at Nuts and asked, "Are you completely insane?"

157

Nuts replied, with a quote from an episode of The Three Stooges, "He's mad, mad I say!" ending his comment by imitating a cuckoo, which led to another report being filed against Nuts to management.

Driver 44, "The Friesion" Bucking, Bucking

The Friesion had to be the dimmest Taxi man in Ireland, as common sense or even self-preservation wasn't part of his mind-set.

The Airport taxi rank, known as the "Kesh," which was the hardest and roughest taxi ranks in Ireland to work, mainly hardcore Dublin taxi men from the inner city who didn't like "culchies" (that's someone not from Dublin). For those stupid enough to park in the Kesh, go to the toilet, or leave their car for any reason; on their return, they would find brake-fluid poured over their cars, windows smashed, their car aerials bent, tyres slashed, taxi roof sign stolen, or glue placed in keyholes.

Six foot seven, weighing three hundred and fifty pounds, the Friesion was a giant of a man, his hands were like shovels; his party trick was picking up the back of a car and placing it at a ninety-degree angle.

After dropping a fare at the Airport, he decided to park in the Kesh. He blew into John, "Driver 44, Bucking parked here, in the Airport."

John considered he was plane watching, never thinking for a second anybody could be that brain-dead to park in the Kesh, particularly him being the thickest culchie in Ireland. John replied, "Okay, Driver 44, taking a break to view the birds."

Being a huge man, the Friesion drove an Opel Berlina, which was quite a big car back then. Even so, getting in and out was a problem for him. As he entered the Kesh, he followed a taxi in. Not wanting to get out of his car, he beeped his horn and waved to the other driver, who gave him the middle index finger to "fuckoff," but the

Friesion took it as confirmation that he recognised him, and so he continued following him. Within a minute, a group of four Kesh men were banging on the Friesion's window. "Fuckoff out of here redneck!"

They thumped his roof and kicked his car door. But the Friesion was having none of that, so, once outside his car, he stood towering over them, who were now all raising their heads to look up at him.

Grabbing the closest one by the throat, he picked him up off the ground, and threw him like a rag doll against the car beside him, causing its front window to smash. The other two looked at him in shock; one was brandishing an iron bar trying to hit the Friesion solidly on the shoulder.

But the Friesion looked down at him and punched him in the face with such ferocity that blood shot out everywhere. The other two unsuccessfully attempted to run at him, throwing punches and kicks.

As a consequence, his big fist came smashing down and caught one of them on the head, who was in the end knocked out cold. The last guy standing took out a knife and tried to stab the Friesion. Waving the knife, left to right, he managed to cut him across his arm, but the Friesion didn't feel it or even notice it.

On the second attack, the Friesion grabbed him, trapped his arm in a vice grip, and pulled it out of its socket as he turned it backwards, until it broke like dried wood. The sound filled the Kesh, while the onlookers were now running to the assistance of their friends on the ground, who were screaming or unconscious.

In a blind rage, the Friesion picked up the iron bar and raising it over his head, with the white of his teeth

160

showing, he screamed, "I'll bucking kill all of you bucking bastards."

One of the Keshmen raised his hands and said, "Stop, for the love of God, stop."

Sitting on the bonnet of his car, the bar still in his hand, the Friesion was breathing heavy when he was accosted by a Dublin Taxi Driver.

"Look, it got out of hand here, let's shake on it, and leave it at that."

The Friesion reached out his hand and they shook.

Afterwards, he went to the toilet to clean up his arm, took a towel and tearing it down the middle, he wrapped it around the cut on his arm.

He got back into his car. John called out, sounding like he was stressed "Driver 44, are you receiving me? Are you okay?"

Apparently, some radio drivers who worked the Kesh, had blown into their Base controller and told him what was happening, who in turn phoned John.

Without a flinch, the Friesion picked up his mic and called John back. "Driver 44, were you looking for me?" John replied, "are you okay?"

The Friesion replied, "Bucking fucking Dublin bucking bastards broke my aerial."

John responded, "Remind me never to get on the wrong side of you, is it true one of them went to hospital?"

Before he could answer, a Cop tipped his window, and the Friesion was forced to step out again. The Cop asked him if he had been assaulted.

In the meantime, other drivers assembled behind the Cop, waiting to hear if the Culchie would grass on their friends. "No one assaulted me, and anyone that says they did is a bucking liar."

The Cop left, and thirty minutes later the Friesion picked up his first and only fare at Dublin Airport.

An American couple walked out from arrivals, pushing a trolley filled with luggage.

The man was wearing a ten-gallon hat, while the woman was as big as a sofa. She shouted at him in a very disappointed tone, "They've got taxis here Jeremiah."

The Friesion stood out to help with the luggage. Jeremiah looked up at him and said to his wife, "They have bloody giants too, Marta." They both got into the back of the taxi and told him, they were heading to the Gresham Hotel, asking the Friesion, if he knew where it was.

He replied in the thickest Cork accent, that most from outside Cork could never decipher, "Of course I bucking know where the bucking Gresham bucking hotel is."

Marta asked Jeremiah, like she was speaking to a deaf person, loudly and very slowly, "What did he say? Is he speaking Irish?" Jeremiah took out a copy book and tried to pronounce an bhfuil Bearla agat, the Irish for "Do you speak English?" Instead, Jeremiah pronounced it, "Anne bo-fuel bear-la ag-at?"

The Friesion looked at him and said, "What are you bucking talking bucking about?"

Marta replied again, this time even louder, "Did you understand him?"

Jeremiah, now getting annoyed, replied, "I'm not deaf Marta, I'm trying to speak Irish."

However, Marta's attention was soon taken by the Georgian houses in Drumcondra. "Look Jeremiah aren't they adorable?"

A young kid was riding a piebald horse from Temple Street flats. Marta got her camera out, snapping the kid. Turning onto the top of O' Connell Street, which was the second left turn the Friesion made since leaving the airport, both left wheels came off his car, straight down on its axel, causing the car to flip over.

Marta was now screaming, "It's an earthquake! it's an earthquake! we're going to die!" They all continued banging their heads together as the car kept flipping over, until it rested on its roof.

Both ambulance and the fire brigade service were called, but thankfully no one was too badly hurt. Jeremiah and Marta booked into the Gresham and where never heard from again.

The Friesion's car had been totalled; by the Kesh Taxi Drivers who had loosened the nuts on his wheels when he went to the toilet.

Although he never returned to the Kesh, the Friesion was awarded the name "Tiny" by the drivers of the Kesh and the story of his fight became legendary.

Driver 69 Gorgeous George, "Vicky's Fantasy Fulfilled"

Vicky always wanted to try a threesome with a woman, Robyn, on the other hand, only wanted men. It was something they had fought about regularly.

Before she got married, Vicky had been with a few girls in college and enjoyed oral sex with them, granted not as much as she had been enjoying sex with George over the last months.

George was the perfect sexual partner, and she knew who the ideal woman would be. Her friend Amanda was just her type, dark hair, kissable lips, huge tits, small waist, and a tight ass. They went to yoga together, shared their secrets, and their girlie talks normally involved a few bottles of wine. Besides, Amanda had revealed her fantasy to Vicky about "trying it on with a woman."

She was in her late thirties and hadn't had sex in over four years. Vicky bought her a vibrator for her Birthday and Amanda regularly joked about it by saying it was the best sex she ever had.

She had also been engaged to a guy for seven years until he ran off with someone else, blaming her for being sexually boring, which was the reason why Amanda became even more insecure.

Knowing she would be very easy to manipulate, Vicky told George of her sexual craving and who she wanted to bring to their party as she fondly called it.

Of course, George was up for it, his only concern being if Amanda had money. Vicky replied, "She's fucking loaded," and informed George about her background.

Vicky had arranged for George to pick her and Amanda up from town. Robert was away working so, she had the perfect opportunity to act and simply told Robert that she was going out with the girls and would be staying over in Amanda's house.

By two am Amanda and Vicky had already drunk way too many cocktails as well as a line of coke which Amanda took to Vicky's surprise.

As planned, Vicky called the Base for George, and twenty minutes later, he walked into the restaurant, causing every woman's head to turn in his direction.

Amanda had her back to him so, it was only after he came up behind her and whispered, "Your Taxi is outside!" that she had the chance to really look up at him. He was wearing a tight T-shirt that revealed his six-pack and his blue eyes were staring down at her. Her eyes were glued to his crotch, her mouth open, and suddenly she was speechless.

Vicky replied, "That's great, we will be with you in a minute."

Amanda sighed, "He is fucking gorgeous, did you see the body on him? fucking hell Vicky, what I would give to ride him."

Vicky asked "Would you be into a threesome with him? I know I would be for sure."

Amanda responded, without thinking, "He's what wet dreams are made of."

Vicky leant over and put her arm around her and said, "Let's see if we can get him interested."

Amanda smiled and said, "Girl you land him, I will be your friend for life."

Vicky replied, "Thought you were already."

166

They both laughed, and got into the back seat of George's car, "Firehouse please," Vicky directed George. Then she whispered into Amanda's ear, "Let's kiss and see if he's interested."

Amanda didn't need any prodding; she put her hand through Vicky's hair and kissed her. Vicky pushed her tongue into her mouth, and after twenty seconds Amanda pulled away. They both laughed nervously.

Vicky said aloud for George to hear, "God, I've wanted to kiss you all night, can't wait to get you home girl."

While winking at Amanda, she said to George, "I hope we didn't embarrass you."

George replied, "No actually, I was getting quite turned on."

Amanda's mouth opened as she gave Vicky the thumbs up behind George's seat.

Vicky responded by saying, "I'm sure a guy like you must have had plenty of threesomes."

"I have, but never with a gay couple," George replied.

Vicky said, "So you enjoy watching me kiss her like this," grabbing Amanda's head and kissing her passionately, her tongue down the back of her throat, she fondled Amanda's tits, then kissed her neck and whispered in her ear, "Pull the tits off me, he will go mad for it." Amanda put her hand into Vicky's blouse and caressed her tits, both of them enjoying their kiss even more.

It was George who broke them apart by saying, "Yes, that certainly gets me turned on."

Vicky winked again at Amanda, "I'm sure you don't really mean that.." her eyes looking at his, in the car's rear-view mirror.

167

"If you could see my cock right now, you will know just how much that turned me on," George replied.

Vicky pulled Amanda close and said, "Grab his cock;" but Amanda was getting nervous, so Vicky prodded her, "Go on, you're not chicken, are you?" Vicky replied to George, "My girlfriend wants to see it."

George pulled over the car and turned around looking at Amanda, and as his eyes were melting every part of her, he said, "Sure, jump over into the front seat." Amanda looked at Vicky who was simulating with her hand a cock being wanked off.

As Amanda climbed into the front seat, Vicky felt her ass, George continued to drive, "It's not going to bite, unless you want it too," he laughed.

Vicky put her arms around George's seat, feeling his torso with her hands, and continuing down to his crotch, she told Amanda to open his jeans. Amanda nervously opened each button as Vicky continued to massage his balls from the outside of his jeans.

George's cock was now standing two inches above his waistline. Amanda looked back at Vicky, her lips simulating, "Oh my fucking God!"

Vicky moved behind Amanda's seat and said to George, "Would you like me to finger my girlfriend as she wanks you?"

"Absolutely," George replied.

Vicky brought her hand up Amanda's skirt, her skin soft, she could feel her goose bumps as she used the top of her nails on the inside of her thighs.

Amanda lost rhythm wanking George, her eyes closing as Vicky's fingers got closer to her pussy. From the outside of her knickers, Vicky could feel Amanda's pussy was hot and noticeably wet.

Amanda returned to wank George again while Vicky, now was flipping her fingers across Amanda's pussy; her cum starting to flow as Vicky inserted a finger into her, and then with her other hand she reached under her blouse, and pulled her bra up, so that her huge tits could drop down.

"Do you like them?" Vicky asked George, who was glancing over all the time.

"Absolutely!" he said, his cock now bulging. "They're fucking amazing!" Amanda smiled.

Vicky removed her hands from Amanda, and came in between the seats, first kissing Amanda, saying to her, "We have him, he is up for it, keep wanking him," then she mouthed George's cock over Amanda's hand, sucking him. Just as George parked outside Amanda's house, "Are you coming in?" Vicky asked George.

"Definitely," he replied.

Amanda was first out of the car, and grabbing Vicky aside she asked, "Is this really happening?"

Vicky replied, "Do you want it to happen?"

Amanda replied, "Fucking yeah, but your married, what about Robert?"

At the same time George was just locking his car door fixing his jeans, Vicky said, "Look at him, do you think I'm giving that a miss?"

They both laughed as Amanda opened the door, she said, "She needed to go to the toilet."

Once she was gone, George grabbed Vicky and started to kiss her. "Guess you are going to get your fantasy," he whispered. Vicky left him and went into the toilet where Amanda was washing her crotch.

Vicky said, "Wow, you are eager."

Amanda replied, "You know I haven't had fucking sex in over four years, apart from a vibrator, and I have a fucking Aphrodite God in my front room, with a fucking huge cock." Vicky told Amanda, that she was on the pill and asked her if she needed condoms.

Amanda replied, "Girl, I would have his baby any-time, it would be like having God's baby."

Vicky said, "Let's give him a show and fuck him silly." They both walked into the front room holding hands, laughing as Vicky kissed Amanda in front of George who was sitting very comfortably in a seat.

Vicky slowly, unbuttoned Amanda's blouse, revealing her large breasts. Next, she unzipped Amanda's skirt, which fell to the floor, French kissing her, and unclipped her bra, her tits bouncing out. Vicky slowly caressed them, and as her fingers circled the soft crevices of her areola, Amanda's nipples grew harder. Vicky started to suck them as her other hand slid down her body into her knickers, fingering her. Slowly, she kneeled, and as her lips started kissing every part of Amanda's body, she re-moved her knickers, to lick between her thighs. Amanda was now sighing and moaning, still standing but quiver-ing. Vicky's tongue licked and explored the lips of her pussy, tasting her, until Amanda started to cum, stopping her.

Vicky came back up calmly kissing and teasing her, and after taking her tongue out of Amanda's mouth, she whispered, "Not yet, my love, do the same to me now..."

Amanda now completely naked, and with her nipples standing to attention, looked at George and smiled.

He said, "Wow, you are amazing."

Then, she unzipped Vicky's skirt, kissing her as she put her hand down her knickers and fingered her.

Vicky encouraged her friend by repeating "like that," and later, "yes, give me three fingers."

"Shout, so he can hear!–Do you want me to stretch your pussy? here's three fingers."

Amanda repeated her words, smiling over at George.

She slowly pulled Vicky's knickers down her legs and pushed them apart, only to resume her slowly ascent with her tongue up her right leg until she stopped at her pussy. After opening her lips and tasting Vicky's cum, she came back up and said, "Did you like that?"

Vicky replied, "Amazing, let's do him now."

Vicky turned, looked at George, and said, "Join us." They both slowly undressed him, caressing his body, each taking turns to kiss him and each other.

All the while, Amanda kept looking at George like he was from another planet as she unbuttoned his jeans.

Then, they both pulled down his pants, and as his cock popped out, standing straight up, their hands started covering every part of his body; Amanda focused on fondling his ass while Vicky kept caressing his balls. Vicky started sucking his cock; Amanda soon joined in so that both could kiss and lick his cock between their mouths, kissing each other.

Afterwards, they all lay on the floor. Amanda eager to fuck him first, with her hands started awkwardly jerking his cock. So, George took her hand in his and showed her how he liked to be touched, all the while kissing her gently. Vicky on the other hand, opened Amanda's legs, licked her ass, found her pussy again, and kept slurping up to when Amanda started to cum.

George sensing Amanda's eagerness laid on his back and told her to squat over his cock and sit right down on it. Like an obedient servant Amanda followed his instructions. Vicky settled behind Amanda, to squeeze and stretch Amanda's nipples, caressing her tits and kissing the back of her neck as Amanda rode George like a cowgirl. Vicky's fingers circled Amanda's g-spot, felt her body tightening, about to explode and at the same time, she could feel George's cock as Amanda raised her ass and went back down, like a steel pole.

Finally, Amanda screamed and gushed all over George's groin. Vicky thought she was urinating, until George said, "We have a gusher here." He put his arms around Amanda and rolled her over, onto her back. Immediately, he went down to consume her, and invited Vicky to join him.

Again, George raised his body over Amanda and penetrated her, "Oh my God, I'm going to cum again!" Amanda screamed. Vicky was head deep between George's ass and Amanda's pussy, licking his balls and her pussy.

Feeling Amanda's legs tightening, Vicky knew she was about to gush again. Vicky had never seen a gusher before; it was like she was urinating as her cum shot out of her pussy.

"No more please, give me a rest," Amanda begged George. He kissed her and said, "Take a rest, I will be back." He moved on to Vicky, riding her hard, making her cum over and over. Amanda lay looking at them, mesmerised at how George was fucking Vicky.

Later, Vicky suggested they do a line of coke.

Twenty minutes later, they started over again, Vicky sucking Amanda, still on her back on the bed with her legs open as George fucked Vicky doggy style from behind, changing places. George pounded Amanda as she was bent over the bed. Vicky was on all fours over Amanda as George had his head between her ass sucking her pussy as he fucked Amanda at the same time. Vicky wanted to see Amanda gush again.

George placed Amanda on her back and as he was kissing her mouth and circling her breasts, he moved down, fingering her at the same time as Vicky kissed her mouth, stretching her nipples and squeezing her tits.

George felt Amanda was about to cum and he told Vicky, "There she blows." Amanda once again squirted cum in the air like a gun as her body twitched, "Oh my God!" Vicky replied.

After that, both George and Vicky got between Amanda's legs, flipping their tongues together, kissing and licking Amanda's pussy dry.

Four hours later Amanda was woken by the rocking of her bed. She opened her eyes to see Vicky straddling George's cock, riding him like a horse.

Amanda said, "God, it wasn't a dream!"

Vicky bent over and kissed her as George pulled back the bed sheets and got in between Amanda's legs, saying, "I love the taste of pussy first thing in the morning." He sucked her until she was very wet, Vicky was kissing her, looking at Amanda's eyes opening so wide when he penetrated her. Vicky kissed her as George made love to her so slowly and with such intensity that she gushed within minutes.

It was seven am when George left Amanda's house. Vicky walked him to the door, and said, "That was amazing, you are fucking amazing!" they kissed.

Amanda was sitting up in the bed when Vicky came back into the bedroom. She looked at Vicky, removed the sheet that covered her, her legs wide open, she said, "Girl, I'm yours forever." Vicky walked over, wrapped her arms around her, and kissed her gently while asking if she had a great night.

Amanda replied, "I never enjoyed sex as much in my life, wow, it was fucking amazing."

Vicky kissed her again and asked, "What about us, did that freak you out?"

Amanda replied, "I have fantasised about fucking you for years, I enjoyed absolutely every fucking second, when are we doing it again? I hope you got that God of a man's number."

Vicky nodded her head and said, "Girl, we are going to have fun with him, wow my pussy is fucking sore." Amanda put her hands between her legs and said, "My pussy lips are swollen, that fucking cock of his was like a jackhammer, and as for his body," her mouth wide open, "do you know I've never gushed with a man in my life until last night? Jesus, he is fucking gifted."

Vicky told her she wanted to hook up with him and her again and that it was going to be their secret.

Amanda reached out and kissed Vicky and said, "No one would ever believe me in a million years if I told them about him," smiling into Vicky's face, she added, "and you."

The following months were very profitable for George from fucking Vicky and Robyn every second week and Vicky and Amanda every other week.

Vicky had persuaded Amanda that it wasn't fair that George was losing money and he had to pay his boss, so Amanda offered to fund their fun.

George bought his next car from the proceeds of his physical training as he called it.

Nuts and the "Man Eater"

In the eighties, a nightclub called Sachs, in Balls-bridge, was famous for its over fifties.

Any given night, bar Monday, Dublin's baggage handlers as they were called could be found in Sachs. Most were married, separated, or had serious mental issues.

The young Taxi Drivers called it the "Zoological Gardens." Sitting in their cars in the dead of the night, they were subjected to watch fifty- or sixty-year-olds, or women as old as their mothers, giving head or getting shagged in the car park behind the hotel.

Two or three drivers would be usually sitting and narrating as an old age pensioner would try to open her legs and fall over, some old bony arse revealed from Khaki trousers.

Most if not all the young Taxi Drivers that ranked outside Sachs were looking for a quick shag, and the older women who attended knew it and normally would wait outside with their friends for the younger drivers to arrive.

The "man-eater" was known to most drivers who worked Sachs. She was unnaturally tall with masculine features, big hands, and huge feet. She wore a very bad blonde wig that covered her thinning grey hair. She suffered from bad body odour and had a prominent mole on the right-hand side of her face. She went to Sachs most nights, looking for a guy who was pissed enough to fuck her.

Mostly striking out, she would be the last to leave, hoping on the four o' clock crawlers to be either so drunk or desperate to decide to bring her home. The man eater,

177

once in the back of the taxi, had to be watched closely, she had no reservations about masturbating her male friends behind a Taxi Driver's seat. On too many occasions, the guys would sober up and question if she was a *he*; at that point some barfed while others just wanted to get out of the car. One or two started to scream, and it was not unusual to hear some guy ask her, "What the fuck are you?"

It was past four in the morning when Nuts dropped off a fare in Ballsbridge, and passing Sachs, a hand flagged Nuts down. She opened his front passenger door and got in beside him. She introduced herself to Nuts as "Alice" and asked him if he could bring her to Kilmainham or to his place.

Making a joke, Nuts keyed his mic and called John. "Away with Wandery Wagon to Kilmainham," which was code for grandma psycho. Alice told Nuts she thought he looked cute, and she could eat him.

Nuts using his impersonations, answered her in Jerry Adam's northern accent and said, "There will be no eating the Taxi Driver, what happened to your last boyfriend, did you eat him too?"

The man eater tapped Nuts shoulder with her big fists, and said, "You're funny."

Nuts keyed his mic and replied in his little red riding hood accent, "Oh Grandma, what big hands you have."

Alice responded, "I have a big fanny too; you're that small, you would probably get lost in it."

Alice lifted her blouse and her saggy cellulite tits like half water filled plastic bags, dropped to her bellybutton. She said, "Would you like to feel these?"

Nuts, without losing a breath, replied in Jimmy Cagney's voice, "Shucks, I didn't bring my climbing boots."

Alice asked Nuts if he found her attractive, he replied, "You're like Chewbacca from Star Wars."

"Is that the Princess character?" she asked, as she reached in between Nuts legs, groped his crotch, and said, "Would you like a wank?"

Nuts in Adolf Hitler's voice replied, "Take your handen off-en the cock-n."

Alice just laughed again and said, "You're very funny." She moved closer to him, her body odour in his nostrils.

Nuts still as Adolf said, "Look at Dee window Fraulein." As Alice turned to look at the window, Nuts hit the brakes hard sending her face first into the window.

She screamed, "Your fucking mad, what did you do that for?"

Nuts replied, "To get Dee handy off-n me mickey."

Alice screamed at him, "You've marked my face; I'm going to sue you."

Nuts replied again as little red riding hood, "How would you know? with a face like yours, and what a very big face you have indeed grandma."

Alice punched Nuts in the head so hard he lost control of the car; it mounted the curb puncturing both front tyres.

Nuts calmly called John, in Captain James T Kirk's voice, "Kirk to Base, Enterprise is down beside the canal, got a hit from a Klingon."

John couldn't respond because he was bent up laughing along with the fleet, at what Nuts said a minute earlier. John eventually responded with, "Is your passenger all right? Do you need an ambulance?"

Nuts responded in Buckets accent, "It's not an ambulance. What this one needs is a fuckn horse box; she carries her own fucking airbag with her."

Alice, still in shock, raised her fist to Nuts face and said, "I'm going to sue you for every fucking penny you have."

Nuts replied, as Chewbacca, with a loud growl, keyed his mic and said to John, as Matlock, "John, could you inform a Garda Siochanna, I would like to report a sexual assault against my person, this oversized lady, well I think it is a lady, groped my private region causing my car to veer off the road."

Alice shouted at him, "You're fucking Nuts!" to which he replied to John, "She would seem to know my name, she called me Nuts. Any drivers around that might give me assistance."

John called out a Charlie, and five minutes later, Jumping Johnny arrived just before the Cops. He asked Nuts, "Who's your man in the dress?"

Alice tried to tell Johnny that Nuts was mad, but he got a spasm attack, his head violently jerking back and forth.

Alice screamed, "Jesus, what's happening to him?" Nuts reached out his hand, which was holding two pens in the shape of a cross, and said, "Come out, you demon, come out."

The Cops didn't see that but saw Alice punching Nuts in the face again. Jumping, Johnny had also recovered from his attack; the first Cop got out of his car and said, "Would you look at who we have here. It's Alice," two passers-by started to sing, "Alice, Alice, who the fuck is Alice?"

The Cop said, "What's the problem this time Alice?"

She replied, "This fucking lunatic thinks I'm a Klingon and he is Captain Kirk, or Adolf fucking Hitler."

The Cops looked at each other and asked her if she had taken any drugs tonight, which sent her off on one.

"You're asking me if I'm on drugs, this fruitcake smacked my head into the windscreen."

Nuts, for the first time, spoke to the guard, again imitating Matlock's persona, "Guard, if I may tell you the events. I picked up this lady outside Sachs, she informed me she was travelling to Kilmainham and said, she wanted to have sex with me. She exposed her breasts and told me she had a swimming pool in between her private regions and asked me if I would dress as a sheep for her. I think she has some psychological issues. When I turned that corner.." Nuts pointed over at the junction, "..she grabbed my private parts and said she wanted to eat me. I lost control and collided with the curb."

The Guard replied, "Don't worry son, we all know Alice." He asked Nuts if he could follow them down to the Garda Station to make a complaint. Nuts replied there was no damage barr the two tyres, and if she paid for them, that would be the end of it.

A cheque for fifty quid was received three days later in the Base addressed to Driver Nuts.

Peter Meets Psycho Sandra

Barmen, Busmen, Taxi Drivers, they all work in an environment that attracts schizo's, dipso's, and weirdo's, an occupational hazard, or the joys of the job, depending on how you look at it.

Sadly, some of these bunny boilers became obsessed with them and started to stalk their victims, sometimes with an innocent gesture or a display of thoughtfulness that turned into being persecuted by someone with aggressive and violent tendencies.

Psycho Sandra was the definition of a sociopath.

Originally, she was a dash girl, that's to say, a girl who sits beside the Bus Driver on every journey and would end up having sex at the terminus. The bus drivers, almost all married, affectionately named her the "Bawnogue Gobbler" as she had perfected the art of blowjobs and lived in Bawnogue in Clondalkin.

Once experienced, never forgotten, eventually, her reputation of causing havoc to every married Busman she met, ended her escapades within those circles. Therefore, she moved to the opposite side of the city and on to Taxi Drivers.

Her first victim was Colm Driver 77, Known as "Mr Perfect," because everything in his life was exactly as it should be for a man retired from the Army. I guess his life was conditioned a certain way; his car perfectly cleaned every day, his nails manicured, his clothes ironed to perfection, his wife always flawless, his house like a showroom, and his reputation beyond reproach.

Of course, that was true until he picked up Psycho Sandra in his taxi. Sandra was in her early thirties, dark hair and quite attractive; her perfume was like her clothes, seductive while mysterious.

She always wore black stockings and sexy lingerie tastefully hidden and knew how and when to reveal it. Colm picked up Sandra coming from the primary school where she worked. She was full of chat and flattery, admiring his physique and commenting on his appearance, she asked Colm to stop so she could get some shopping.

Carrying some heavy bags back to his taxi, Colm got out and helped Sandra. As she reached out her hand, she turned her shoulder in, revealing her cleavage and her laced bra, and catching Colm glancing, she asked him for his name saying, "It was so refreshing to be carried by a true gentleman I felt so safe."

From that first encounter, every time she called, she asked for Colm. She focused on Colm's chauvinistic side and became the helpless woman.

One evening, after collecting her, she asked him if he could put a bulb in an overhead light, which of course he did. Sandra offered him a cup of tea and said she needed to get dressed but left the door ajar just enough to let Colm see her strip out of her clothes, revealing her sexy lingerie as she changed dresses.

When she came back in, she said, "I hope you didn't mind, I didn't realise the door was open."

Colm's face now red.

"Sure, your married, you have seen it all before," she said, noticing Colm's bulge in his trousers.

Two weeks later, she rang for Colm to pick her up again. This time, she pretended she was running late and asked Colm if he wanted to wait inside. Again, she got dressed with the open door and watched Colm trying to look through the crack of the door.

Re-adjusting her red G-string, she walked out and said, "Do you think this is sexy?"

With his eyes transfixed on her, he replied, "Yes."

She asked him if he was horny, his face now glowing, he nodded. So, she bent down, took his cock out, and sucked him slowly.

In fourteen years of marriage, he never experienced oral sex; for him it was mind blowing. Then, Sandra straddled him and rode him until he exploded.

Immediately after, the guilt filled his heart, and he said, "This was a mistake, I'm married, you know that."

Sandra replied, "Don't worry, it's our secret, I won't tell anyone." She walked back into her room and got dressed, making small talk on the journey without a mention of what had happened.

Two days later, Colm completely consumed with guilt, went up to the Base to tell John about what happened and looking for his help. But John found the whole thing amusing and basically boring, even more so when Colm told John it was the first time in fourteen years he had ever cheated.

John's reaction was typical, "Ahh man, you should get a fucking medal for that, sure, if God meant us to be monks, he would have removed our balls, don't sweat it, are you sure you don't want to keep tapping her?"

Colm replied, "Oh no, ahh fucking no."

To Colm, it was the end of the world. He begged John to make excuses for when she called again, maybe that he was gone on holiday with his family and forced him to swear he wouldn't tell a soul.

In order to help his friend, John devised a plan, "You have to go on the missing list, so let's pretend your engine is fucked, leave it a few days in a garage I know, and I'll tell her you're off the road, hopefully, she will move onto someone else."

That same evening Sandra called, and John told her what had happened to Colm, so he sent Buckets of Blood to pick her up.

Colm returned to work a week later; Sandra called on the same day, but she was told Colm was still off the road.

Unfortunately, Sandra knew the truth about his return from Buckets after posing as Colm's sister-in-law. She also asked Buckets if he had ever been up to his house, to which Buckets answered that he dropped off his wife a few months ago from the Northside Shopping Center. Sandra went on with her questions like "how far is it from here to Colm's?" and Buckets replied, "Ahh, five minutes, I guess."

In the end, Sandra, pretending to be stupid, replied, "God, I'm terrible with directions and names, what's the name of Colm's Road?" and Buckets told her "Elm Mount Avenue."

Early into a Saturday morning at 3 am she called John and asked for Colm; again, John told her he was off the road, so she asked for a taxi to go to town and John sent Poor Peter to collect her.

Peter knocked on her door and she came out all smiles, telling him she would be just with him. Carrying a hand-bag, she got in beside Peter.

"Your off to town, is that right?" Peter asked her.

She waited until Peter informed John he was engaged to town, then she told Peter she needed to stop off to her boyfriend's house first, who lived in Elm Mount Avenue.

As Peter drove onto the Avenue, Sandra pretended, she couldn't remember where he lived and asked Peter to drive slowly until she noticed Colm's taxi. Just here, she said, "That's his house!"

Peter stopped across the road from Colm's house and waited for her to get out and to walk over.

Peter was in the midst of turning his car when he noticed her taking a lump hammer out of her handbag and smashing it on the windscreen of Colm's taxi.

Peter Blew into John, "Charlie, Charlie!"

John responded, "Driver 6 is having another Charlie lads." Thinking Sandra was groping him or something similar.

"That lunatic is smashing one of our taxis with a lump hammer." Hearing where they were, John quickly realised whose car she was pulverising and asked Peter, "What is she doing now?"

"She is walking around his car smashing anything that has glass."

"Driver 22, are you on the scene?"

Buckets of Blood had just arrived and in no time, he was out of his taxi, and close to Sandra, who swung the hammer at him, menacingly.

Buckets instinctually gave her a punch and she was out cold. The bedroom lights on Colm's house just went on as Buckets picked Psycho Sandra up and lobbed her into the back of Peter's car.

"Get her out of here, now!" he screamed.

Peter called John, "Driver 6, Buckets, oh I mean Driver 22 has just put this lunatic into my car, she's unconscious, he told me to get her out of here."

John replied, "Why is she unconscious, Peter?"

"I didn't see anything" he replied.

"Ahh, you're certainly getting the hang of this business Peter," John replied sarcastically.

"What type of woman walks around with a Lump Hammer in her handbag?" Peter responded.

"I know a few" John joked, "where are you now Peter?"

Just as Peter turned onto the Malahide Road and was about to reply to John, Sandra came around and punched Peter in the face. "Charlie, Charlie, she's awake, she's awake!"

Another punch landed into Peter's face, "Where's my hammer?" she screamed," Where's my fucking hammer?"

Peter, now dazed and shitting himself, replied, "You left it at your boyfriends house."

Holding his microphone open, he told her he couldn't sit there on the Malahide Road, so that John, in turn, could hear where he was.

Cars started to beep their horns. and Peter asked if he could just move his car over to beside the field, again keeping his mic open. "Everything is going to be alright," Peter told her as she curled up in his back passenger seat.

Back to the crime scene, Buckets was helping Colm, who had just opened his door, to find his car smashed to pieces. He was wearing his nicely pressed pyjamas that matched his slippers.

Viewing what had happened, Buckets asked him if he did see who it was.

Colm replied, "No" and continued looking around Buckets, observing the other houses to see if any were awake or looking out their windows, but there was none.

"It was the blonde one, Sandra from Donnycarney," Buckets told Colm.

Colm's face went white, "Sweet fucking Jesus, where is she now?" Colm asked Buckets.

"In the back of Driver 6's car unconscious."

Colm's wife called down the stairs, "Is everything okay, is it safe?"

Colm replied, in an extraordinary calm voice, "Yes, my love, with you in a minute."

"Why is she unconscious?" Colm asked, partly knowing the answer because of Buckets reputation, "I had to give her a smack, I don't hit women unless they need it, she tried to clobber me with a lump hammer."

"She did what?" Colm replied.

"Yeah, the fucking mad bitch was swinging a fucking lump hammer, that was some fucking psycho shit."

Colm needing to attend to his wife, asked Buckets if he could keep Sandra away from his home just for tonight, that he would pay him to watch his house until the morning.

"No problem, man," Buckets replied.
"Look, I don't know what shit your into, but I'll keep her away. Tell your missus someone is targeting taxis. Don't say anything else."

Colm just looked at Buckets and nodded, taken aback at how smart Buckets was to come up with an explanation for this nightmare so quickly.

Sandra, on the other hand, was starting to feel the pain in the side of her face. "Did you fucking hit me?" she screamed at Peter, punching him again.

"I certainly did not," Peter replied.

Sandra told him to bring her back to Colm's house.

"I can't do that, madam," he replied.

"Don't you fucking Madam me!" Sandra was just about to launch herself into another assault when Peter's back door opened.

It was John from the Base, who, with his face partly covered, sat menacingly beside her. Sandra looked at him and asked, "Who the fuck are you?"

He replied in his original Belfast accent and which Peter hadn't heard John use before as he had lived in Dublin for nearly twenty years.

In the staunchest northern accent, he spat out his words to her, "You fucking don't know me lovely," taking out a brown glass bottle with no label. "See this bottle of acid, I'll fucking lift your fucking face with it."

Sandra, now shaking, started to cry.

Grabbing the collar of her coat, John pushed her face into the seat, holding the bottle beside her eyes, "Do yee see this? I'll fucken scar yeah, stay a fucking away from Colm's house or I'll drop down to your house in Donnycarney and fuck you up."

John got out of the car and disappeared into the field beside the road.

Peter was speechless, Sandra whispered in a crackled voice, "Take me home please."

Minutes later, John called Peter in his familiar Dublin upbeat accent, "Driver 6, are you okay?"

Peter replied, "Taking this lady home."

"Okay, that's great, call me when you're free."

Sandra didn't say another word, just paid Peter and got out.

"Driver 6 free in Donnycarney, God, that was terrifying." "Peter, what is the colour of her door?" John asked. Peter looked back and seen it was red as she disappeared and closed it.

"It's Red John, why?"

"Just for our records, no more taxis for that lady."

"She's no lady, think I will have a black eye in the morning," Peter replied.

John told the fleet he was just stepping out for a wee minute, an ongoing joke for when he was using the toilet. But, this time, he was using the public phone across the road in case the call was traced back.

He picked up the receiver and dialled the number she gave when ordering the taxi.

Sandra answered, "Hello."

John went into character, and again in his staunch Northern accent, "I told you I know where you fucking live bitch, your door won't be the only fucking thing red if I hear you acting the bollox with my mate, got it?"

Sandra was frozen in fear, her hands trembling as she looked out her window, thinking he was outside.

John screamed down the phone, "Do you want me to come down there and fuck you up?"

She replied through tears, "No, please, no, I promise I won't bother him again."

John just hung up.

On Base day, that's when the drivers come in to pay for the use of their radios, Peter asked John, "Where did the accent come from and why did he act that way towards her?"

John replied, "Psycho's like that don't listen to reason, or fear being reported to the Cops, there is only one language they understand, violence."

Peter asked him if he would have carried out his threat to pour acid over her.

John smiled and replied, "Don't think pouring cough medicine over her would have had the same effect," and picking up the same brown glass bottle, he removed the lid and had a swig, both laughing.

After that, Sandra moved on to another taxi company and another victim.

Driver 58, "One Ball Paul"

Having one testicle didn't stop thirty-nine-year-old Paul, a father of three children: Sofia, aged seventeen, Elizabeth, aged eleven, and little Paul, aged three.

Paul certainly was an oddity in the taxi business being happily married. He met his wife Joan when they were just teenagers, and she was, as he called her, "the one." Joan had a bad delivery on their last child, so they agreed that rather than risk her having a hysterectomy, which was described to them as a painful and traumatic surgery, Paul gets a vasectomy.

After some consultation and examinations, Paul gave a sample of his semen for analysis, and everything seemed to be fine.

Paul's brother, Kevin, was a taximan too. He was three years older than Paul, had been married for only two years, twenty years ago, and had been single ever since.

Kevin and Paul were very close, so, he offered to drive his brother down to Lesson Street for the operation which was supposed to take less than an hour. Kevin said he would go off and do a fare or two and drive him back after it was done.

Paul walked into the Georgian building at four o' clock, still nervous about the procedure. The receptionist smiled and asked him to wait in a room, pointing to her left, where twenty minutes later, a doctor came in with a nurse.

"We have some news; you might want to sit down." Paul expecting they had found cancer, fell down into the seat. But the doctor took a piece of paper from his folder and read it aloud; "The sample specimen is void of sperm cultures."

Paul looked at him and said, "What does that mean? Have I run out of soldiers?"

The doctor looked at him, shaking his head, "No, you are infertile Mr. Kenny."

Paul looked at him for a moment and said, "I have three children, that's impossible."

The doctor replied, "We have checked it three times, there's no mistake Mr Kenny."

Paul asked him, "Could he have become infertile recently, like in the last three years?"

The doctor told him, "You were born with an abnormal Y chromosome, you could never father a child."

At that point, Paul was getting angrier.

"That's impossible, are you saying my Joan was fucking someone for the last eighteen years, and my kids aren't mine?"

The doctor repeated, "You were born with an abnormal Y chromosome; you could never have fathered a child Mr Kenny." Paul got up and left the room.

He walked out and onto the street in a daze, trying to comprehend what he was just told. Everything in his mind was saying they had made a mistake; sure, his children all physically looked like him.

Forty minutes later he walked into his house. Joan got closer and putting her arms around him, she asked, "How's my brave soldier?"

"I'm fine, I didn't get the snip."

Joan looked at him and said, "What do you mean? You didn't get the snip? It was your idea to get it."

Paul replied, "They told me I didn't need it because I'm infertile."

Joan looked at him and said, "That's mad, sure we have three children."

Paul replied, "that's what I told them, they said I was born with an abnormal Y chromosome and could never father a child."

"They got it wrong, probably a mix up or something." Joan responded, "Are they calling me a whore? We should fucking sue them."

By chance, three days later, Paul picked up a solicitor from Stephen Hennessey and Goldsmith, one of Dublin's best legal firms. Paul told him about what happened, and he offered to take his case pro bono dependent on a blood test from his children confirming he was their father. He told Paul it could be worth fifty or sixty thousand pounds in compensation. Paul couldn't wait to tell Joan.

After he dropped off the solicitor, he went home to tell her, but as soon as he mentioned testing the kids she said, "Do we want to be dragged through the Courts for years and everyone knowing our private business?"

Paul was adamant that he wanted his good name and his children's names cleared of any slur. It became a topic of argument between them, over the next months. Ordinarily, Paul would concede to Joan in arguments, not wanting anymore fights, so, he let her think he had given up on the idea.

One Wednesday, Joan went shopping as usual with the girls; Paul, taking advantage of her absence, brought little Paul along with a sample of his semen to a clinic where he had arranged testing.

Two weeks later he got the results. It confirmed Paul was infertile and that little Paul was not his son.

The test also identified a very close relative, suggesting that one of Paul's siblings, could be little Paul's father. Considering that Paul only had one brother, he soon realised that his brother Kevin was the father of his children, and that Joan had been fucking him for almost twenty years.

At that moment, he knew his entire life was a lie and everything he believed in was a joke. For a second, he thought about ending his life, but growing angrier, he thought that Kevin and Joan would probably love that.

Therefore, he set about proving what the medical profession was saying was the truth, and that his wife and brother had cheated and lied to him for his entire married life.

At times, while looking at Joan in the middle of the night while she slept beside him, he desired to kill her. He thought about how he could continue sitting in his brother's taxi knowing he had been fucking his wife for almost two decades while Paul remained faithful and how his brother must have been laughing his head off.

Paul knew Joan would never admit it, so he went to "The Fixer," a Taxi Driver with IRA connections. He was the go-to man in Dublin's taxi world, from supplying guns and drugs to setting people up.

After spending fourteen years in Port Laoise Prison, for organising a bombing campaign, the guy that grassed him up was placed into witness protection.

From prison the Fixer had planned the kidnap of his mother. Forcing the rat to surface, and thanks to the assistance of a few friends, the rat woke up in the driving seat of a car with two kilos of cocaine in his lap and half a mile away from Port Laoise prison, where an anonymous tip to the local Cops had the rat arrested.

Still using his new identity, the rat was held in Port Laoise prison overnight, were the Fixer cut out his tongue and hacked off his cock and balls. The rat bled out on his way to hospital.

The Fixer could sort out any problem, from kneecapping child molesters to breaking the ribs of woman beaters. Paul had helped the Fixer in the past and knew he would help him plan his revenge.

Paul didn't wish for them to be murdered or maimed, he just wanted them humiliated and exposed; he wanted them to feel the way he did.

All it took was one trip to Port Laoise Prison to visit the former cell mate of the Fixer as nobody met the Fixer directly. It was ironic how, even after his release, the Fixer still used the prison to organise hits and special business deals as they were called.

It was a brilliant idea because, who would ever consider investigating a prison for crimes committed outside?

Paul met the Fixer's former cell mate and called in the favour and by the time Paul got to the gate of the prison on the way out, a guard told Paul, "That favour is being paid."

A script for Paul to follow was left on his back-passenger seat when he woke up the next day. First, Paul took a loan out from his credit union. He employed a private investigator the Fixer called Frank. He sat Paul down and told him he could call it off right now, looking at Paul to see if he was serious, Frank could see the hate in his eyes.

Paul said, "No, I want them to feel my pain."

Frank tapped Paul's home phone.

Frank told Paul to confess to his brother that he was going to get one of the kids checked because the doubt was eating him alive.

Meanwhile, Frank had been deliberately travelling in Kevin's taxi to get a sense of the man. Frank was very astute and quickly realised that Kevin was a weak minded and an easily led man. Frank knew Kevin would ring Joan the moment Paul told him, and on queue, ten minutes after Paul told his big brother, Kevin called Joan.

Frank, in turn, dialled the Base for Paul; he picked him up twenty minutes later, and together listened to the tape recording.

Kevin's voice said, "He's going for a test, saying it's eating him alive, what are we going to do?"

Joan answered, "I'll convince him not to."

Paul started to cry uncontrollably on hearing his Joan scheming to keep the lie covered up.

Kevin said, "This can't get out, it will fucking destroy me Ma and Da."

Joan replied, "Fuck your ma and da, my kids will never speak to me again, I will be labelled the biggest whore in Dublin."

Kevin, trying to lighten up the conversation, said, "I really need to see you Joanie, badly need you, I'm fucking gagging for you."

Joan replied, "Would you fuck off about meeting? you and your cock has done enough damage."

Kevin responded, "Wasn't just my cock Joanie, you were the one who started fucking me if my memory serves." After that, Paul asked Frank to switch off the tape recorder, saying he had heard enough.

That evening Joan was unusually tentative to Paul, exactly as Frank had predicted, hugging him and kissing him. But her words kept playing over in Paul's mind.

Joan, feeling her husband's tension asked him "Yer not thinking of that test anymore sure yer not."

To him, her words were like ice being poured through the veins of his heart, anyway, Paul mustered a smile and said, "No, I have put it behind us, strange you mention it, Kevin was just saying today, I should get the test done."

Putting his arms around her, he said, "I was thinking you and me should go away, just the two of us, a second honeymoon, what do you think?"

Joan kissed him and said, "Yes, that's what we need, it would be great," and grabbing Paul by the waist, she said, "I love you; you know, yeah."

Paul, still consciously thinking of her words on the tape recorder, replied, "Of course, I love you too".

The next day Frank called the Base for Paul again, and when he got into Paul's car he said, "There's been another call, what the fuck did you say to her?" He switched the recorder on, Kevin answered.

"Hello, Joan" immediately she blurted out, "What the fuck are you playing at?"

Kevin replied, "Calm down what's up Joanie?"

"Don't you fucking Joanie me. Paul told me you want him to get the test."

Kevin replied, "He's only blaming me because he's not man enough to tell you himself." There was a pause then Joan said, "He wants to go on a second honeymoon."

Kevin laughed, "You better meet up with me soon, you know how horny you get in the sun, do you remember when we all went to Tramore and Paul got sunburnt, he was asleep, and you were sucking the cock off me when Sofia walked in, you said you were fixing my trousers. God, she wouldn't believe that now, how old was she then?"

Joan replied, "Four."

Paul could feel his heart cave from within, how could the woman he trusted his whole life betray him and her children? Paul wanted revenge; he wanted Kevin and Joan to feel the humiliation he felt.

The next part of the plan involved Paul getting his brother infected with an STD. Most Taxi Drivers knew the sexually transmitted disease units in Dublin, so Paul drove to James Street hospital STD unit and parked outside. Two hours later a familiar face was walking up; it was Rachel, one of the prostitutes who worked in Tandies, the brothel on South Great George's Street. He opened his door and called her over.

Clearly, she was embarrassed to see him, as she tried to make excuses. But Paul interrupted her, and with no preamble, asked her if she wanted to make two hundred quid. Her embarrassment disappeared.

"Who do I have to kill for that?" she asked.

Paul asked her, "I take it you have an STD!"

She replied, "Yeah, I've gonorrhoea, fucking pussy is on fire all weekend."

Paul told her the reason he wanted her to infect his brother, showing her the letter from the clinic.

Rachel replied, "Jesus, that's some fucking dark bitch you married," and the next thing she said was, "where and when."

Paul knew Kevin's movements as well as how much he loved girls in leather miniskirts with black stockings.

So, two nights later Rachel got into Kevin's taxi wearing his desired clothing. Paul gave her a small device to record him, so he couldn't lie his way out of it when Joan got the clap.

She switched it on when Kevin was getting erect; Rachel asked Kevin, "Do you have anyone in your life?"

Kevin replied, "Nobody of any importance."

Rachel pressed him, asking, "Are you sure you don't have a bit on the side, good looking guy like you."

Kevin replied, "Yeah have a horse I ride now and then." Five minutes later, Kevin could be heard saying, "I want to fuck you so badly."

Rachel replied, "Let me suck your cock first."

Kevin cried out, "Jesus did you bite me?"

Rachel responded by saying, "Get that cock into me and fuck me now."

An hour later, Rachel was collecting the two hundred pounds after giving the tape recorder back to Paul.

After listening to it he asked Rachel why she bit his cock, she replied, "Gonorrhoea gets straight into the blood stream when the skin is broken, trust me, his skin was broken," she laughed and got out of Paul's car.

Paul feigned to fall off a ladder and hit his groin in order to avoid any sexual interaction with his wife.

Three weeks later, Frank met up with Paul and gave him a handful of new tapes. "Listen to this one first." Frank handed Paul the tape. Paul inserted it into his recorder and listened to Joan's voice saying to Kevin she needed to meet up, Kevin asking her why, eventually making her beg for his cock, asking her if her little stoking horse had her all horny and she needed a real man. Joan begged him saying, "Please, Kevin, you know I need your cock, please give it to me."

Frank handed Paul another tape and said, "Listen to this one it's a cracker." Paul inserted it and pressed play.

He now heard Joan's voice screaming at Kevin, "You gave me the fucking clap, you dirty fucking bastard, I have the clap!"

Kevin replied, "How do you know I gave it to you?"

Joan replied, "Because I'm not riding anyone else, you fucking cunt."

He asked her, "How do you know it wasn't Paul?"

Joan responded, "Because he hurt his cock remember." Joan told Kevin she went to her doctor because she had a green discharge from her pussy, and it burned every time she went to the toilet. The doctor told her she had gonorrhoea and to tell her sexual partners. Kevin didn't say anything for a while; Joan asked him, "Have you been riding someone else?"

Kevin replied, "Never, Joanie, my kitten, you're the only woman for me."

Then, he asked her if she was in a swimming pool, used someone's towel, or sat on a toilet seat in a restaurant or pub, desperately trying to shift blame away from himself.

Frank gave Paul the last tape and said, "Here, you will enjoy this one."

Kevin's voice, "I had to go to James Street Hospital and have a fucking burning rod shoved down the hole of my cock, you gave me this fucking disease, you fucking whore."

Joan replied, "I didn't, I'm supposed to be going away next Friday with Paul, and I have the clap."

Kevin responded, "Sure, give him a ride, when he gets it, blame him, he's that thick, he'd believe anything you tell him."

Any reservations Paul had about putting a stop-to his revenge was eliminated after hearing that tape.

Months of planning, months holding a towel to his mouth crying in the bathroom, it was all coming to an end. He had booked a room in the local pub, inviting both his family and Joan's, and all of their friends.

All people they cared about would be there, except for Kevin. That invitation was going to be given on the day, so he couldn't warn Joan. It was going to be a surprise wedding anniversary party, and afterwards, they would be off on their second honeymoon.

The night before the party Paul grabbed Joan and told her, he was better down there. But Joan made an excuse saying she was having a bad period, and instead she offered to give him a hand job. He replied, "Sure, we'll have plenty of time on our honeymoon."

Then, he handed her a letter addressed to her, saying, "It must be from Sofia's school it's a tape, must be the French lessons she wanted."

Afterwards, Paul went to work, and Joan opened the envelope in which she found a letter and a tape. The letter read, "Hello you don't know me, but I saw you and your husband Kevin together the other day and realised he didn't tell you that he has the clap. I'm a prostitute that Kevin has been riding regularly for five years, I tape all my punters, here's a copy just in case he denies I exist. I am so sorry; I didn't realise he was married as he never wore a wedding ring."

Meanwhile, Paul had called Frank and asked him to monitor the phone." Two hours later, Frank dialled the Base and hooked up with Paul, "Listen to this!"

Frank was laughing, while Joan's voice, in the background, crying and screaming was saying "I'm a horse you ride now and then, nobody of any importance, you dirty bastard, you told me you weren't riding anyone."

Stunned, Kevin, at first, hadn't a clue what Joan was talking about.

"Calm down Joanie," Kevin tried to interrupt her, "I haven't been riding anyone but you, you're my kitten."

Joan played the tape; he could hear his own voice saying, "Nobody of any importance." Joan clicked the tape forward, he heard himself say, "Yeah have a horse I ride now and then," Joan clicked it forward again, Kevin's voice saying, "I want to fuck you so badly."

Joan cried into the phone, "Kevin, what type of dirty animal are you? I had three kids for you, you tell me you love me, and you give me the fucking clap. I have been fucking and sucking you for eighteen years and this is how you treat me? you bastard."

Kevin hung up, Joan tried to ring him back twice, but he didn't answer.

The following morning Paul went down to the local pub and met the sound technician Eddie, another friend of Frank's. Paul and Eddie worked on the sound for the night's entertainment; they placed the projector screen in the line of the door for everyone to see. Frank had also organised a guy to video-record the night's events.

Paul told Joan that he had booked a table for them in the pub. A quite romantic night just for the two of them. Joan was particularly quiet from the evening before, her eyes swollen from crying. Paul asked her if Kevin had called.

She snapped back at Paul, "What would he be ringing here for?" Then, she apologised, blaming her period for her bad humour. Later that day, Paul called Kevin and finally told him about the surprise party and that everyone was going, from their parents to their uncles, aunties, and all the locals and friends. Kevin tried to make an excuse by saying he had a job, but Paul insisted that he had to be there.

By eight thirty the room was packed with over a hundred of Joan and Paul's family and friends, balloons, and poppers ready to be released. As Joan applied her lipstick, Paul came up behind her and said, "Tomorrow it will be a different world for us, Mrs Kenny." She feigned a smile back to him; they kissed the kids goodnight.
Paul whispered to each one of them he loved them with all his heart, he grabbed Sofia, who was babysitting and said I love you no matter what.

Ten minutes later, they were walking through the doors of the pub to a rapture of applause, balloons falling from the ceiling and streamers from poppers covering them. A big poster, wishing Joan and Paul a "Happy Anniversary" was pinned on the wall.

Paul's parents were the first to congratulate them, then Joan's parents, followed by all their family and friends. Last to come over to them was Kevin. Joan's disdain for him was obvious but Paul wrapped his arms around him and whispered in his ear, "How's the clap?"

Kevin jumped back and looked at him in shock, then Paul grabbed Joan by the arm and said, "Come on girl, you have to give my big brother a hug!" swinging her in his direction. Joan and Kevin hugged awkwardly.

Everyone started to call for a speech. Paul stood up on the stage and picked up the microphone, blowing into it, to make sure it was working, and after thanking everyone for coming, he turned to Joan and said, "Get up here girl."

Reaching out his hand, Joan jokingly protested and stood up on the stage to another round of applause.

Paul took her hand to the sighs of the women, he looked into her eyes and said, "Eighteen years ago we walked up the aisle, I was the happiest man in the world, you told me I was your soul mate, you gave me three beautiful children. I thought the angels had made you, that you were the most honest and faithful woman I had ever met, then," Paul looked over to Eddie and nodded. Paul continued, "Then I found out the truth."

Everyone looked at each other confused. Joan looked at him and said, "What's going on Paul?" He let her hand go and stepped away from her. He shouted to Kevin, "Come up here, my big brother;" and once by his side, he took his hand.

Paul looked out at all the familiar faces and said, "The two people in the world I trusted with my life." Paul looked at Eddie again and nodded.

In that moment, the sound of Joan's voice filled the room. "Kevin what type of dirty animal are you, I had three kids for you, I have been fucking and sucking you for eighteen years, you told me you loved me, and you give me the fucking clap." Shock and disgust were etched on everyone's face, while the projector started to show the pictures of Kevin holding each of Paul's kids at their Christenings, on which Eddie had also inserted on the picture in big letters "Proud Dad."

Paul let go of Kevin's hand, and picking up the microphone, he said, "You see, folks my big brother was fucking my loving wife for every year of our marriage." Paul nodded again to Eddie. Kevin's voice now filled the room, "You better meet up with me soon, you know how horny you get in the sun, do you remember when we all went to Tramore and Paul got sunburnt, he was asleep, and you were sucking the cock off me when Sofia walked in, you said you were fixing my trousers to her. God, she wouldn't believe that now, how old was she then?" Joan replied, "Four."

Joan started to cry, Kevin asked Paul to switch off the sound, but two of Franks henchmen walked up onto the stage and put themselves beside Kevin placing their hands on his shoulders. Besides, a menacing big woman stood beside Joan, while three others locked the doors. Paul looked out at his mother and father who were now crying, his friend's faces in shock and disbelief because of what they were hearing.

Paul continued, "Can you imagine how heart-breaking it is to find out you're infertile and at the same time to find out the love of your life, was fucking your own brother. He fathered my children." Eddie had edited the tape and looped Joan's voice, now playing loudly, "Kevin, I had three kids for you, Kevin, I had three kids for you. Please, Kevin, you know I need your cock, please, Kevin, you know I need your cock, please give it to me."

Tears now were rolling down Paul's face, so he picked up the mic and said, "And, do you know what my loving brother thinks of her?"

Paul nodded to Eddie, and suddenly Kevin's voice filled the room again, "Yeah, have a horse I ride now and then, a horse I ride, nobody of any importance." Joan was standing, tears dropping from her face. Paul brought the mic to his mouth wiping away his own tears.

"Folks, in the tried and tested tradition of giving presents on your anniversary, we were supposed to be celebrating our eighteenth anniversary tonight, which is signified by porcelain, elegant and sophisticated. So, I got an elegant and sophisticated prostitute to give my brother and my loving wife the Clap. Don't think any of you ever thought of a present like that. By the way Joan, you are a dirty fucking whore and I want a divorce, and Kevin," Paul punched him in the face, knocking him to the ground. Paul said, "You can have your horse. I'm out of here; I have a plane to catch."

Nuts and the "Animal Rights activists"

Another pastime for Nuts was crashing functions in the North Star Hotel, which was next to Connolly Station. While waiting for a train to arrive, Nuts would usually just walk in and check the board to see who was holding a seminar or meeting. Mostly he did it on his own, but if another driver from Kilmore Taxis was there, he would drag them with him.

One Thursday evening, while waiting for the nine twenty Belfast train, Nuts and Jumping Johnny walked into the reception. Nuts noticed the function Board advertising a meeting for the RSPCA. Nuts said to Johnny, "there will be plenty of food and drink at this one." So, the two of them walked into the packed function room, to see on stage, a woman who was banging on about wild dogs roaming the streets in the North Inner City.

As he scoffed a Danish pastry and helped himself to the free coffee Johnny said to Nuts, "What about the junkies roaming the streets off their heads?".
A toffee-nosed busy body interrupted them and asked which section of the RSPCA they were from.

Nuts in a perfect Australian accent, replied, "We are here for the Hedgehogs, those beautiful little blighters."

Johnny nearly choked on his Danish.

The busy body asked Nuts who had invited him to the meeting.

Nuts replied, "Look, Sheila, I have travelled all the way from Skippy Land, and I noticed while I was in your Phoenix Park a catastrophe waiting to happen."

She asked Nuts his name, Nuts replied, "Edward Murphy, although people call me Eddie."

After that, she went on stage to speak to the orator, who in turn, publicly announced they had a visitor all the way from Australia who came to the meeting because of his concerns for the wildlife in the Phoenix Park.

She reached out her hands clapping, and said, I would like to introduce you to "Eddie Murphy." When she said his name, she looked puzzled, while Jumping Johnny started to laugh and said, "Let's get out of here," but Nuts refused, "No, let's wind them up."

Thankfully, the age of those attending was mainly over sixty and hadn't seen Beverley Hills Cop and didn't realise Eddie Murphy was black.

Nuts walked up to the podium, shaking hands with a few elderly attendees and while thanking them for coming, he got to the stage where he also thanked the speaker and got everyone to give her a round of applause. Abandoning his Australian accent for Axel Foleys, he introduced himself.

The busy body looked at him in amazement when he spoke; Jumping Johnny, on the other hand, remained in the back of the room, laughing. After introducing himself for the fourth time, Axel said, he came there because of a life and death situation in their Phoenix Park, and to ask for help. Pointing at everyone in the front row, he said, "I need you, you and you. I got a hire car the other day while I was driving through your beautiful Park at six in the morning."

Then, he began talking about how much he likes the smell of the grass first thing in the morning or getting side-tracked. He also mentioned he knew people who smoke grass but that was a different meeting.

Anyway, he kept narrating about that time when he noticed a dark batch, he thought was paint on the road and drove over it, how the car was shaking; and to make it more real he thumped the podium.

"First it was very loud, Bang, bang, bang," he hit the podium three times, "then it started to get a little quieter, less shuddering of the car," he hit the podium two times a little quieter, until it stopped. "I stopped my car, got out, and noticed a Hedgehog stuck in the wheel of my car. A hedgehog little sticky fella, well he is a dead fella now. So, I had to walk back, and there was a procession of hedgehogs going across the road, no warnings for motorists, no hedgehog warden with a big lollipop stick, nothing."

Then again, Nuts side-tracked and started to tell the audience about when he was a boy, he had a hedgehog called Henry. Just as Nuts finished, Jumping Johnny got a spasm, and the busy body screamed, "He is having a fit!" Everyone now was looking at Johnny.

Nuts walked down to him, knowing his crises only lasted less than a minute, he put his hand to his head and said, "You healed my son, you're healed."

It took three more tries until Johnny stopped. Some people in the audience started to clap; Nuts walked back up on the stage, thanked everyone, asked them to donate any funds they had for a hedgehog warden to be appointed, told them they were a lovely audience, and that they could go home.

Most got up out of their seat, as the speaker ran back up on the stage telling everyone it wasn't over yet and thanking Mr Murphy for his passionate plea on behalf of the hedgehogs.

Johnny said to Nuts, as they walked out the door, "Fucking hedgehogs, you are fucking Nuts," they both laughed.

Driver 6, "Poor Peter and his Classmate"

It was five am on a Sunday morning. Peter had just dropped his last fare of the night in Gardiner Street when a guy in his late thirties came out from a Bed and Breakfast and waved Peter down. He opened the door and jumped in. The first thing he said was, "Boss, you fucking have to get me to Tallaght in a mad hurry." Peter called John and said, "Driver 6 engaged to Tallaght." John replied, "Driver 6 away to Tall-a-hat-chy."

The passenger asked Peter to "fucking floor it, man." Peter asked him if he was alright, and his passenger replied, "Man, I was fucking the girl friend and fell asleep after doing the biz, you know what I mean."
Peter nodded with a look of amazement on his face.
"There's going to be fucking killings, man, me missus will be cracking up," Peter, still looking at him like he just dropped from a spaceship.
"Man, me missus is up the duff, and she doesn't do the biz, you know how that plays out. I need to be jockeying, you know what I mean, not natural not to be rogering some snatch, bet you must be getting your hole every night doing this cabbing shit, pussy galore I bet."

Peter tried to respond but he just kept talking, "last fucking year she got preggers, and I was tapping her sis, fucking her like a good thing, great rack, and sucks like a fuckn hoover, lying cunt told me she was on the pill. The fucking bitch got preggers too, man, her brothers are mad things from Bal-e-er.

They were hunting me for weeks, nearly lost me bollox and all." He looked again at Peter and said, "come on man, floor it."

Peter replied, "I'm going as fast as I am legally permitted," his passenger ignoring his reply kept talking, "me girlfriend was fucking upset yea, know what way they get, flowery fuckers some of them, wants me to leave me missus, like that's never happen-n, cause I love her and all but no way could I leave me kids." Peter asked him how many kids he had, "five with me missus and four with different mad ones."

Peter looked at him in amazement and said, "You have nine kids, how old are you?" and asked him if he was working.

He replied, "Don't have time for working, I'm only young, like, I'm twenty-eight in June, I do a bit here and there, you know what I mean like." He rolled up his sleeve and showed Peter a gold watch. "Do you like that?" he asked.

Peter replied, "Yes, it looks very expensive."

His passenger replied, "Stroked that the other night from a fuck'n American, thick fucker stopped me at the corner of Sherriff Street, must have just got off a train from Connolly. He asked us to take his picture, gives me a big fuckn Pentax camera. I gets him to stand in a doorway, thick mother fucker walks in like a dozy bastard, whacks him over the head with his camera, he goes down like a bird I use to be fucking, blood everywhere, takes his wallet, five hundred fuck'n quid, a few credit cards and this watch, sold the camera. Got fifty for that, do you want to buy this watch?" he asked Peter.

"No, your fine," Peter responded.

"I have one at home, not as good as that one though. By the way, I'm Tomo," he stuck out his hand to Peter, they shook. "What's your name?" Tomo asked.

214

"Peter."

"Saint Fuckn Peter, that's an omen or what. Me ma has your statue on her bed, do you want to do me a solid Peter, make an easy fifty?" Tomo asked him.

Peter, not understanding half of what he was saying, replied, "What do I have to do?"

Tomo replied, "Nothing mad like, just need an alibi for tonight. When we get up to mine, I'll pay you like, and then we will pretend we're bolloxed drunk. I'll tell me missus I met you last night, you were in me school, and we went on the piss." Tomo took out a fifty-pound note and a twenty and gave it to Peter. "Here take it, that 'ill cover the fare and fifty on top for being me alibi."

Peter tried to give it back, but Tomo refused.

Peter asked him if his wife would be up when they got there.

Tomo replied, "Yeah more than likely, fuckn kids wake at five." Looking at his watch, he said, "bollox it's fuckn nearly six now."

It was already daylight when Peter turned onto Fearthercairn Park in Tallaght. Tomo pointed to his house and Peter stopped a few doors up.

Peter noticed a blue Hiace van parked awkwardly on the path. He asked Tomo if his brother in-law drove a blue van. Tomo replied, "yeah, how do you know that?" Peter pointed at the van, Tomo responded, "fuck, fuck, they're gonna fucking kill me, man, you have to save me, just pretend to be me schoolie right." Peter in a state of panic, agreed and got out of his car.

Tomo wrapped his arm around Peter's shoulder and said, "me good owl schoolie, I love yea."

215

They pretended to sway as they went up the foot path. The front door opened. A very pregnant woman was standing in a purple bathrobe; her breasts had tattoos, with a face of a demon. Tomo called out to her, "Sharon, looks who I met last night, it's Peter, I went to school with him."

Sharon, like a ninja, grabbed Tomo by the collar and swung him onto the ground screaming, "Do you think I'm fuck'n thick or what, you went to fucking school with him, he's fucking twenty years older than you, was he kept back for being a retard, you smell of fucking pussy."

Sharon's brothers came out and started kicking Tomo in the stomach as he lay on the ground.

Tomo screamed "Peter, save me man."

Peter turned and started to run. Sharon grabbed him by the back of his shirt, screaming at him, "Where are you going retard?" Her face was beside his, he could taste the gin she was drinking earlier. She grabbed him by his balls and yanked them hard. Peter went down to the ground in pain, and she kneed him in the face.

Peter was knocked out; he woke what he thought was a few minutes later and everyone was gone. Tomo's front door was closed, and the van was gone. Peter got up off the ground and made his way to his taxi.

Looking in the mirror he saw that his nose was covered in blood so he took his handkerchief and tried to clean his face.

Then, with the swelling starting to rise, he picked up his mic and called in, "Driver 6, I've been assaulted."
He told John the story, who in turn, asked him if he really wanted to get the guards. John knew it was a waste of

time and they would just deny it, plus those type of people were not good to have as enemies.

Peter put his hand in his pocket and found the seventy
pounds; he keyed his mic and said, "On second thoughts,
no, I'll put it down to experience."

Two months later, Peter was dropping a fare to
Fearthercairn Avenue he asked his female passenger if
she knew Tomo and the woman surprised questioned Peter on how he knew him.

Peter told her part of the story about picking Tomo up
and dropping him off, so, his passenger started to laugh
and said, "You're the fuckn retard!"

Peter looked at her in his rear-view mirror; she was
still laughing, and while trying to catch her breath she
said, "Sharon's my best mate, that Tomo is a dirty bastard, fucks everything. He got his comeuppance that night
I can tell yea. Sharon's brothers kicked the fuckn shite
out of him. He won't be riding anyone for a long time,
dirty bastard, he was even riding Sharon's mother, she's
a dirty whore too, said he forced her, me bollox, that one
can't close her fucking legs to walk, he got their babysitter pregnant, fucking a seventeen-year-old. She was the
one he was fucking the night you picked him up, her father is out for Tomo's blood. He will fuckn cut his balls
off if he catches him."

Peter replied that he didn't know anything about it and
that he was just helping him to the door when Sharon
smashed his face. He also told her that he briefly considered going to the guards and pressing charges but decided
not to as they seemed to have enough trouble.

Hearing that, his passenger came between the seats
and whispered in Peter's ear, "You're lucky you didn't,

they would fuckn burn you and your family alive, they're psychos. Sharon's me mate and all, but I wouldn't get on the wrong side of her. They're all fucking bonkers, drugs, and gear. Sure, there was killings in the shopping centre yesterday with Sharon's sister, now she's defo a mad bitch, was called out for riding her ma's boyfriend but she wasn't riding her ma's boyfriend, it was her ma's ex-boyfriend, fucking possy of Cops trying to rip them apart, hair and teeth flying, took, five fuckn Cops, you were right not to get the Cops involved Mister," she said to Peter, as she paid him and got out.

Nuts and "Marriage Guidance Counselling"

Another favourite pastime of Nuts was breaking up couples, using his skills of impersonation and adopting roles of characters he had seen on TV. Nuts would play out an episode in the confines of his car. His goal was to break up a couple, keying his mic for John to hear; sometimes bringing John in for support.

In the mid-eighties Quincy M.E, Colombo, and Sherlock Holmes were hit TV programmes. Quincy was a medical examiner always busy creating back stories of how a suspect could have committed the crime. Colombo portrayed a bungling idiot who masked his intelligence as stupidity and who always managed to push the accused to admit his crimes. Sherlock Holmes, on the other hand, used reverse psychology or behavioural science to create different possibilities that might have caused the perpetrators to act a certain way.

These two characters obviously had a profound effect on Nuts so much so that he could adopt the full mannerisms of each character, including their voice, at will.

Moreover, Nuts absolutely loved working Valentines Night, giving the amount of "Tracky Heads" which was the standard attire back then, for young guys in their early twenties, and that included a shiny track-suit along with bright white Addis runners. They were Nuts favourite victims.

Looking back, I think Nuts might not have been as crazy as we all thought. The way he picked his target and then manipulated the conversation around to his purpose was genius.

For most people, Valentine's Day, was a time for romantic gestures. For Nuts, it was open season on his favourite prey. Once in a taxi, the first thing a newly engaged couple did was tell the Taxi Driver that "they just got engaged" followed by the engagement ring being displayed.

For most normal people, it was charming, for Nuts, it was an invitation to slowly rip a couple apart all in the name of fun. Asked why he kept doing it and Nuts would always reply, "They will thank me some day." Of course, he answered in President George Bush's voice.

Sadly, when it comes to foresight, most men are extremely limited, add alcohol to the mix and the male ego is a recipe for disaster. So, the scene was set for Nuts' first victims of Valentine's Night.

It was eleven pm, and after a romantic dinner ~~over~~ and a proposal the couple was, as expected, on cloud nine. Like an episode of Mills and Boon, the Fiancé had his arms around his woman, keeping her safe on a taxi rank.

All loved up, he opened the door of the taxi for his bride to be, he got in beside her all smiles. But, unfortunately for them, Nuts was driving. As usual, within ninety seconds they told Nuts "They've just got engaged."

Nuts in a sudo American accent congratulated them and keyed his mic. "Driver 80 away to Finglas have two more for the good Counselling Centre, in Drumcondra."

John knew by his accent that he was in character, which meant that Nuts was going to have fun with his guinea pigs. Nuts left his mic open.

Instinctually, the female passenger asked what did he meant about the good Counselling Centre in Drumcondra.

Nuts adopting his Quincy persona replied, "I'm studying to be a psychotherapist and do two days a week in the Counselling Centre in Drumcondra, Marriage Guidance Counselling is mandatory for couples who wish to get married. I expect I will see you two shortly." Nuts now looking in his rear-view mirror at the guy said, "The questions are usually based on reverse psychology, there not that hard."

Looking sternly at him, Nuts continued, "I'm sure you would have no difficulty answering them. Anything regarding exams or tests sent the fear of God in most Tracky's."

Judging by the stunned look and silence, Nuts was setting the scene. "Driver 80, John, didn't you go to Marriage Guidance Counselling last year?"

John replied, "Did you have to mention that Driver 80, those bloody questions were mad, and me bird lost it?"

Nuts replied, "Didn't it all work out in the end, though?"

John responded, "Well I didn't get married, if that's what you mean, knew by those questions we weren't meant to be."

The silence was broken by the female passenger who asked, "What type of questions do they ask?"

Nuts in full Sherlock Holmes said, "Well you see, the male mind is simplistic in comparison to the female. It has been scientifically proven that the male is driven by hormones in their twenties and thirties, so sex is the primary factor sometimes miss-interpreted as love, we call it the lust - love syndrome. Females are ordinarily more foresighted and have more intelligence than males, organised, conscious of the practicality of living together is already considered. Consider this for a moment, not meaning to be impertinent or rude, but normally a couple like yourselves are being intimate, experiencing possibly for the first time your sexual pleasures, idiosyncrasies and obviously learning the joy of sex. Like anything that gives pleasure human beings particularly men, can become addicted to it, most times mistaken lust for love. So, questions and analogies can expose if it is truly love or just lust. The questions save a lot of unnecessary heartache and failed marriages." Nuts turned around to the girl and asked, "What's your name?"

She replied, "Louise."

"Now Louise, you are an attractive and may I say, a very intelligent woman, you know when it comes to living with someone, bills have to be paid, like the rent on your flat, utilities like electricity, gas, food, so you already know that going out three and four times a week will be impossible, going on holidays will be forfeited, you also know it's possible you might get pregnant, and that will have to be budgeting for, prams, cots, nappies, medicines." Nuts asked her if she was working.

Louise replied that she worked as a waitress.

Nuts again, complimenting her, said, "All intelligent women like yourself know that if you had a child, it wouldn't be commercially viable to stay working, wouldn't make sense to pay for a full-time babysitter."

Louise responded, "I wouldn't hand my baby over to anyone to rear it."

He could see the look on his male passenger's face, so he turned around and asked him his name.

"Brendan" he replied. "I will offer you an analogy,"

Brendan interrupted Nuts and asked, "What's an allergy?"

Nuts replied, "No it's not an allergy, it's an analogy, something that could possibly happen to see your response."

Louise was holding Brendan's hand, giving her man support.

Nuts turned up the accent even more. "For example, Brendan, I guess you have single friends around your own age."

Brendan replied. "Yeah."

"Okay, now let's pretend you have been living with Louise for two years, you have a baby, the electricity bill is overdue and with sleepless nights and money strains, your sex life has been reduced to once or twice a week, for five or ten minutes."

Turning to Louise Nuts said, "You are certainly a beautiful woman, but for the sake of the analogy, we are going to say, again pretending, that you have post-natal depression and Brendan is not seeing you as you are today, no makeup, or hair done, no sexy clothes, just a woman struggling to cope."

Nuts turned back to Brendan and said, "Now, let's say you haven't been out with your single mates for nearly a year, and they're all going to Ibiza for two weeks. They call up to you and want you to come out for one drink. Let's say you really want to go out, knowing they are going to have the time of their lives in Ibiza with all of those fit girls in tiny bikinis, so here's the question."

Nuts double keyed his mic, that was code for heads up, here it comes, "You're in a nightclub with your mates and this brunette comes over to you, mini skirt, extremely well developed, looking beautiful and in front of your friends, remember your male ego, and image your friends have of you. She asks you to go home with her or asks you for your phone number. What would you do?"

Brendan paused and said, "Ahh, I would."

Nuts interrupted him, and said in his Colombo accent, "See, if you have to think what's the right answer then you're not ready for marriage."

Louise turned and faced Brendan and said, "You fuckn bastard. Ahh, fucking ahh, I've had a kid for you, I'm manically depressed, and you fucking say, 'ahh', you are a selfish bastard, and here" Louise took off her ring and threw it in Brendan's face, saying, "here, have your fucking ring back, you only want my pussy, you bastard." She asked Nuts to pull over; she got out of the taxi.

Brendan, in a panic, asked Nuts how much he owed him, paid him, and got out too.

Nuts keyed the mic and asked, "Who won?"

Between the eighteen drivers they were all taking bets on how long it would be before she got out of the car, a tenner extra if the ring was thrown back.

John replied, "Eight minutes and seventeen seconds. Buckets won, he was the closest with eight and a half minutes."

Nuts played his CD of Queen he had queued and ready, across the airwaves it played, "Another one bites the dust."

Nuts meets, "Touchy Feely"

Touchy-Feely was an extraverted gay thirty-some-thing who lived in Balbriggan with a death wish or maybe he was a practising masochist. He got a Taxi every Friday from Abbey Street taxi rank after work. In the past, most Taxi Drivers had assaulted him, yet he kept coming back to the same taxi rank, waiting for a different driver to come to the first position. He would try to proposition them straight away before they even got off Abbey Street.

The usual scenario saw the reverse lights of the taxi that would go on, the taxi that would reverse back to the rank, and the driver who would open his door to drag him out. It didn't matter that Balbriggan was a great fare being twenty pounds back then, a driver's reputation was more important.

Touchy Feely opened Nuts passenger door and asked him if he was free. Nuts replied, "Yeah, in you get."

His driver's window got a knock; Nuts put down the window, and another Taxi Driver said to Nuts, "He's one of those queer boys, and he will try to pull your bollox."

Nuts replied in Shirley Temple's accent, "I'm a lesbian, I love pussy."

The Taxi Driver walked away telling two others who were standing beside him, "Your man is fucking Nuts."

Touchy Feely asked Nuts to take him to Balbriggan, taking out twenty pounds.

Nuts took the cash and blew into Arthur, "Away to Balbriggan."

Then, Touchy feely asked Nuts if he ever had his cock felt by a man.

Nuts replied, in a deep Dublin accent, "Yeah me Da, he used to change me nappies, full of shit they were."

Touchy Feely looked at him and said, "No, you don't understand what I'm asking. Has a man ever put his hand down your trousers?"

Nuts keyed his mic and asked Arthur, "Did any man ever put his hand down his trousers?"

Arthur replied, "Not so far, well my doctor has, got me to cough, you know what I mean, playing pocket billiards." He asked Nuts why, he wanted to know, and Nuts replied, "Have this geezer beside me asking if a guy ever felt me cock."

Arthur knew Nuts was in character so played along, "How much is he offering?"

Touchy Feely said to Nuts, "What are you doing telling him what I said?"

Nuts replied, "I don't know what to charge you to pull the bollox off me."

Touchy feely smiled and said, "I will give you another twenty."

Nuts replied, "If I let you touch me, I get to keep all the money."

Touchy Feely responded, "Of course it's all yours honey."

Nuts replied, "Give me the cash."

Touchy Feely gave Nuts the extra twenty and immediately placed his hand on Nuts knee.

As Nuts turned onto Drumcondra Road, he hit the switch at his right foot that immobilised the car, which came to a shuddering stop.

Nuts turned over the engine, it wouldn't start, so he asked Touchy Feely to give him a push to start it.

Touchy Feely got out and went to the back of the taxi, placing his hands on the back of the car and started to push. Nuts hit the switch, the car started, and he immediately drove away at speed with a few beeps of his horn, leaving Touchy Feely standing in the middle of the street cursing him.

Five minutes later, Nuts arrived back on Abbey Street. Two Taxi Drivers came up to him and asked, "Did your man offer you money to grope you?"

Nuts replied, "Yes."

The Taxi Drivers asked Nuts, "What did you do?"

Nuts replied, "I took it."

"You did what?" one of the drivers responded.

"Yeah, I took it and let him feel the back of my car as I drove off."

They all started to laugh, just as Touchy Feely arrived back in another taxi, "You owe me forty pounds," he screamed at Nuts, who casually turned around and looked at him and said as Clint Eastwood, "Did you say I could keep all the money if you felt me."

Touchy Feely didn't reply, Nuts continued, "and didn't you feel my sexy knee, did I make your day?"

Touchy Feely left the rank swearing.

Nuts hadn't heard the last of it.

Gun running Peter

Driver 9, Ram Jam, was required to deliver certain items across the border twice a week as part of an arrangement where he got drugs in exchange for transporting commodities, as they were called, for the IRA.

One of the unusual things about driving a taxi was you very rarely got stopped by the police back in the eighties, whether it was because the Irish police licensed and regulated taxis back then, or Taxi Drivers were considered too thick to be involved in smuggling.

One thing was certain, even when there was bomb warnings and the Irish police setup roadblocks, they always waved taxis through. It's almost funny to think, all a terrorist had to do was get a taxi, and he could go anywhere freely.

Ram Jam had smuggling down to a fine art. For example, he always wore gloves when handling the commodities, that way there was no fingerprints, no such thing as DNA back then. He bought the leather or canvas bags that they were transported in from the Ivy second-hand market in Frances Street so the bags couldn't be traced, and always got one of his accomplices on the day of the Run, to carry the bag filled with balloons making it look like it was fully loaded, to flag him down, where he got into the back of his taxi.

Then, he would burst the balloons, folded up the bag, put it under his jumper, and got out; that way, if he was being followed by the Cops, it would collaborate his story that his passenger left it. The bags were placed carefully under the seats of the taxi, so if he got stopped, all he had to say was, it must have been one of his passengers that put it there, with no forensic evidence and no confession, the Cops couldn't prove a thing.

Two runs a week was his limit, and on both occasions, he always used different taxis, as well as different routes into Northern Ireland. A half bottle of whiskey was always left in his drivers glove compartment, again adding to the scenario that a smuggler would never risk being caught, drinking, and driving with illicit items in the back of his taxi.

The reason for his journey had to be legitimate as well, and that was the easiest part: Ram Jam would wait outside Connolly station and offer four passengers a taxi to Belfast for the train fare, which was about thirty-pounds less than he would get, but it was legitimate, and he had four independent witnesses if he ever got stopped, and just for good measure he carried two empty eight gallon drums that he filled up on cheap petrol on the way back, another commercial reason for his trip.

John, on the Base, was part of Ram Jams' distribution network for light drugs and also played a significant role in organizing unsuspecting drivers to smuggle commodities.

A third shipment was urgently required, and Ram Jam had just finished his second trip the day before, so, Poor Peter was chosen because nobody on God's green earth would believe he was a gun runner.

John called Peter when he was around Coolock and asked him to get him a smoke cod and some chips. The chipper was three doors up from the Base, which meant Peter would park his car at the Base and walk up.

As soon as Peter parked outside, John ran down the stairs and opened Peter's car with a coat hanger, a legacy from his very colourful childhood which he now used to open a car and could hotwire it in two minutes if required.

He took out the screws holding the back seat and left the car open. When he went back up to the Base he asked Driver 9, if he needed, to drop of that engine oil.

The moment Peter walked into the Base and closed the door, Ram Jam put the canvas bag under the back seat of Peter's car, left the screws hand tight, and locked the car behind him.

Two hours later, John manipulated Poor Peter's movements and had him dropping off in Swords, exactly at the same time Driver 9, Ram Jam, broke down with four passengers going to Belfast, that he picked up from Connolly station twenty minutes earlier.

John replied to Driver 9, "Okay, I will get another car over to you." Then, he called Peter and told him, to make his way over to the Lord Mayors pub in Swords, as Driver 9 was broke down, and congratulated Peter as he was going to Belfast.

John filled Peter in, on the places to avoid at all costs around Belfast, and to always keep the Divis Flats to his right-hand side. Peter told John he was familiar with the area as he once sang for the rising stars, but unusual for John, he didn't reply with some smart comment.

Five minutes later, Ram Jam handed Peter sixty pounds and said, "Here, take this and be very careful up there." The passengers were delighted as they were now being driven in a brand-new Peugeot 405, and two hours later, Peter pulled into the Great Victoria Street train station in Belfast. His passengers got out and as Peter was leaving, a kid on a skateboard collided with the front of his car. Peter got out, all flustered, but in that moment, another kid jumped into the back of Peter's car, took the canvas bag from under the seat and left while whistling to his mate that everything was cool. The kid said he was fine and got up off the ground and skated away. Peter was shaken and a bit dazed by the collision, so, when he got back into his car and started back for Dublin, instead of taking the first turn left after the train station onto Grosvenor Road as instructed by John, he missed the turn and eventually, took a left onto the Shankill Road.

Peter's eyes focused on the red, white, and blue painted curb stones as well as the English flags outside every house. He looked to his left and saw in the distance, the twenty story Divis flat complex. He shouted to himself, "Oh my God, it's to my left, it's to my left, Jesus." His heart started to race as he realized he had driven into the heartland of the UVF, where painted murals of Red Hand Commando's and Kill every Finian bastard covered any available piece of concrete. Instead of turning back, Peter went into flight mode and started to speed down the Shankill Road, screaming into the mic for John.

Unfortunately, the radius of the taxi radio signal was just fifty miles. To his left he saw a funeral undertaker, just as a white car rear ended him.

Looking into his rear-view mirror he could see that the driver and passengers were wearing balaclavas. Frantically, his car screeched as it turned onto the next road, hitting a red ford as he miss-judged the turn.

Peter hadn't a clue where he was going, but knew he was more than likely going to be killed. The white car came up behind him again; the passenger now, had a gun out of the window.

Peter started to pray, and while beads of sweat started pouring down his face, he saw a milk float stopping two hundred feet away and blocking the road. Pressing down hard on the accelerator he rammed the milk float; milk bottles and glass went everywhere, and Peter's car pushed the milk float fifty yards until he could get around it. Two loud bangs hit the back of Peter's car, his back windscreen shattered, Peter checked to see if he was hit.

Then, as his car started to bellow smoke from the front, he realised that he was fast approaching a park.

Peter went into survival mode and, using his intellect to keep him alive, he grabbed his taxi identification and driving license and threw it out the window into the bushes.

From that moment, everything felt as if it was in slow motion. In the middle of the road there were two burnt-out cars, two steel poles, and two large barrels put on either side. His body went numb as he drove right into a UVF check point; four large balaclava wearing guys brandishing AKM assault rifles were pointed at him, the white car came up behind him and smashed into the back of Peter's car sending Peter's face into his front windscreen.

Peter soon found himself with a broken nose and surrounded by AK-47's and assault rifles with northern accents who were screaming at him to get his Finian fucken arse out of the car. Peter considered this was it, the end of his life; he had seen the terrible images of burnt bodies that the UVF displayed for television and knew he was going to be one of those.

However, whether it was dumb luck or skilled acting, Peter thickened his posh accent as he raised his hands in the air, his face covered in blood, and said, "I'm a Taxi Driver, I was delivering blood to.." he couldn't remember a local hospitals name, so he said, "Your blood transfusion service."

Two of the paramilitaries dragged Peter from the car, his legs scraping the ground as they threw him at the feet of their commander, who looked down at Peter and said, "Are you English?"

Peter looked up and replied, "Yes."

"What the fuck are you doing driving a Finian fucking taxi?" the commander spat out his words.

One thing Peter knew was that, if they thought he was English, they wouldn't kill him. He had discarded all his identification so all they had to go on, was what he told them. "I'm an accountant from Surrey, I'm from Tandridge," Peter quickly adopted his brother in laws name and address, the commander pointed his gun to Peter's head, and asked him, "Where did you go to school in Tandridge?" Peter could never forget the school his nephews went to, it was called Saint Peter's, his nephew kept saying it was named after his uncle.

The commander grabbed Peter, by the throat, raising him up off the ground, he brought Peter's face beside his, and asked him, "Why are you driving a Finian's fucking taxi?"

Peter had quickly learned in the taxi business to adopt your passenger's persona's and mirror their beliefs, in this case, he knew by painting himself as a criminal, they would think he was one of their own, well that was his thinking. Peter's voice crackled and stammered as he replied, "I cooked the books and stole some money. I've

234

been living in Dublin for the last two years and needed a job."

Through bloodshot eyes, Peter looked at the commander and said, "I didn't mean to steal the money, I got hooked on gambling."

The commander started to laugh and said, "Guess you have lost that job as a cabbie, now get the fuck from here."

Peter opened the car door to get in, a big leather black boot kicked it closed. Peter turned around, the commander had his gun pointing at Peter's face, "We will be keeping the taxi, now away with yeh."

Peter started to walk away slowly, expecting, any minute to be shot in the back, but as he turned onto the next street he began to run. Eventually, he saw an R U C patrol and flagged them down, waving his hands covered in blood, the R U C officers, who after getting out of the armoured cars, immediately got in formation and pointed their assault rifles at Peter who froze with his hands in the air, shouting, "What's wrong with you people, I'm after being rammed, hijacked, shot at, and battered!"

Before his last word left his mouth, Peter hit the ground as one of the R U C officers tackled him from behind. Peter's head hit the concrete hard, and the next thing he remembered was waking up in the back of the armoured car. He was brought to the Royal hospital on Grosvenor Road and carried into the emergency unit.

As the R U C officers placed him onto a bed they said, "You're one lucky boyo, I wouldn't be coming back here, if yee want to be breathing."

Meanwhile, John in the Base was looking at his watch. It was eight twenty, he called out over the airwaves for

Driver 6, "Peter are you receiving me over?" but there was still no answer.

Ram Jam called up to John to see if there was any word about Peter; John told him that nobody has heard from him, "even his wife called me two hours ago, she's getting worried."

Ram Jam replied, "He should have been back hours ago, the fucking egit is probably lost in Monaghan, you know that fucking Gobshite can't follow directions!" John put the kettle on and offered Ram Jam a coffee.

The nine o' clock news had just come on the TV and as John sat into his seat, he started spitting out his coffee, at the same time pointing at the screen, where a picture of eight UVF soldiers standing around a burning "Kilmore Taxi," an RTE reporter said, "a Dublin Taxi Driver was hijacked today, and the whereabouts of the Dublin Taxi Driver is unknown."

Ram Jam and John were in shock, neither of them said a word, but as they watched Peter's Peugeot burn, John broke the silence by saying, "Oh sweet Jesus, what have we done?" before Ram Jam could reply, the phones started to ring.

First, reporters asking for the name of the driver whose taxi was on tv, next, Peter's wife Linda who was sobbing hysterically, until drivers too started to call in on the radio asking if Peter was dead.

To cope with the anxiety, John snorted a bit of coke and offered some to Ram Jam who took a line. Then, he looked out the window tv crews were setting up their aerials and lights. So, he opened the window and listened to some reporters shouting, "we have his name, he lives in Donaghmede Crescent."

When the vans shot off, Ram Jam turned to John and said, "This is going to get messy, the story is, I got a fare and broke down, Peter took over, that's it, right?" He waited for John's reply, "Right?" Ram Jam shouted at John, who finally replied, "Yeh, got it."

Driver 5, Benny Big Shillings, blew into the Base that a news station on the radio was reporting that a body had been found in Northern Ireland. John slumped down into the chair, his hands cradling his face, tears started to flow. Ram Jam barked at John, "I'm out of here!"

"Get yourself together for fuck sake, man!" He left the room, slamming the door behind him. John looked at the TV and could see Linda being interviewed, her daughters holding their mother, all three crying, pleading for the safe return of Peter, and then, suddenly, behind the three of them Peter came up with his nose strapped in bandages and black eyes. He put his arms around them and when Linda turned, she nearly collapsed onto the ground.

John screamed over the airwaves, "Peter's alive, Peter's alive!" Every driver keyed their mikes and beeped their horns as a sign of solidarity. Cars passing Kilmore taxi Base, beeped for days afterwards.

Peter's battered face was across every newspaper, he gave interviews on how he fooled the UVF while in the breath of death.

Two months later, Peter returned to work with his new Mercedes Vito people carrier. He called in, "Driver 6 starting up in Donaghmede," but John corrected him, "Rambo, starting up in Donaghmede."

Needless to say, from that day on, Peter was called Rambo.

"Quiet Ernie"

Driver 52 to everyone on the Taxi ranks of Dublin was "Quiet Ernie," an unassuming soft spoken Taxi Driver who went about his job without getting involved in the usual Taxi antics. Ernie didn't engage with other drivers, his head was usually found face down, reading a book, so much so that even John on the Base seemed to have very little interest in him. That was of course until the day, two detectives and a group of reporters, knocked on Kilmore Taxi's door.

It wasn't unusual for Driver 52 to go missing off the Taxi radio only to appear days later with some excuse like one of his kids was sick or something similar.

Unbeknown to his work colleagues of ten years or his neighbours of decades, not one of them, could have ever imagined or believed that Quiet Ernie, a church going, pillar of society, had two families, and that he had mastered the art of living a double life for almost ten years.

He later revealed that lying was his daily existence, constantly living in fear of exposure and always mentally exhausted, Ernie had two, completely different personas.

To his family in Blessington in Wicklow, he was a musician and a part time Taxi Driver, a father to three daughters aged ten, eight and six and a son aged four; his wife Margret, a voluptuous, fourteen stone, dark haired, thirty-seven-year-old woman, whose timidness and trusting character attracted him to her instantly. Ernie would constantly say to Margret, "You are untouched by the evil of this world."

Reared by staunch Catholic parents in a rural country lifestyle, for Margret, Ernie was an incurable romantic, honest, and dedicated to his family. He seemed besotted and very much in love with her, as even after ten years together, every Monday he would buy her flowers, he would wrap his arms around her, and called her, "his Buttercup." Margret was an only child who inherited her family's farm after her mum and dad passed away; while she wasn't rich, she was, as they call it, "comfortable."

To Ernie's family in Kilbarrack on Dublin's northside, he was a Taxi Driver and a loving father to his two sons aged twenty-two and nineteen, and three daughters, seventeen, fifteen and two. His wife "Joan," who Ernie met when they were in their late teens in a local nightclub, was a forty-two-year-old part time hairdresser, eight stone in weight with bleached blonde hair. Ernie's pet name for Joan back when they were young lovers was also "Buttercup."

This is the story of how Ernie became a Bigamist.

In 1969, when Cathryn, his second daughter was born, Ernie was almost thirty and had already been married for 10 years to Joan.

Back then, he was still working in the same shipping company in Dublin's docklands, where he started when he left school at the age of fourteen, and where he kept working with no qualifications, even after sixteen years of been treated as he would call it, when drunk, "like a slave and an errand boy for all."

Nevertheless, he had achieved the position of assistant manager with the hope of being made manager as soon as his boss, Mr Carroll, as he had to be referred to, was retiring in the summer of 1970.

While the position was open, everyone in the company thought Ernie was a shoo-in; for weeks leading up to Mr Carroll's retirement, Ernie was telling everyone he was going to be made a manager, he was getting a new company car, and that he would soon be his own man and would never have to answer to anyone again.

Two days before Mr Carroll was to retire, he called Ernie into his office, and pointing his finger at a brown leather chair, he told a smiling Ernie, "To sit down."

In his mind, Ernie was already planning how he was going to change all the furniture and get rid of those hideous glass cases that displayed Mr Carroll's golf trophies, but he had to stop fantasizing when Mr Carroll asked Ernie if he heard what he had just said.

Ernie's brain was still trying to catch up, "I'm so sorry Ernie, but you are being let go." Mr. Carroll repeated it again. Ernie kept staring at the glass case, as Mr. Carroll assured Ernie, he would receive a good severance package.

Then, Ernie turned, looked at Mr Carroll, and said, "Am I the only one being let go?"

Mr. Carroll replied, "Yes, the company is taking a different direction, and unfortunately, you just don't fit in with its new image."

Ernie, still calm or in shock, asked who was getting the managerial position. Mr Carroll replied proudly, his twenty-three-year-old nephew, who had just qualified from college was offered the position. Ernie's face went red, as the hatred he had for this man for fourteen years erupted, he spat out his words, "Because I'm from Coolock and don't speak with a posh fucken accent like you, is that the reason, I'm not a good fit. Fourteen fucking years, I have given to this kip, taken shit off you, day in and day out, listening to your sanctimonious shite, well I won't go down easy, I can tell you that."

Mr Carroll said, "And that's exactly the reason you are not management material, you are a gurrier, a buffoon."

Ernie brought his face up to Mr Carroll's, and replied, "Well this buffoon, can prove you have been swindling ten quid a week from the petty cash from doctored petrol receipts for the past nine years, that's over four and a half thousand fucken quid, Percy."

"My Name is, Mr Carroll to the likes of you, how dare you accuse me of such a despicable crime? I'm an honest man, something you wouldn't know being a bastard, not having a father as a male role model when you were growing up."

Ernie left the office as Mr Carroll scolded him, "Go on gutter snipe, get out of my office."

Minutes later, Ernie returned and threw a few receipts on Percy's table, shouting at him, "Here, Mr. Goody Two Shoes, thought you were so smart getting blank petrol receipts from my mate in the BP service station in Tara street, and adding an extra tenner, you're a fucken thief, a fucking low life, stealing from our company, bet you won't be getting a big fat pension when I tell the bosses, more like five years in the nick."

Percy's face lost its colour, as he collapsed into the chair, Ernie acted like he was possessed, like a dog he snapped, he bent down to Percy's face, and said, "See you, you're going to fucking pay me fifteen quid a week, until you fucken die, or else I will spill the beans on you, and have you hauled off to Mountjoy prison." He put his hand in his pocket and took out a bundle of receipts, waving them under Percy's nose.

He laughed as he reached into Percy's jacket pocket and took out his wallet, taking three ten-pound notes, he threw the wallet back into Percy's face and said, "That's this week and next, and when you see me, you can call me Mr Lawless. Got it?" Mr Carroll nodded, Ernie bent down to his mouth and said, "I didn't hear you, speak up," Mr Carroll, through broken snivels, replied, "Yes, Mr Lawless."

That sunny Friday afternoon in July of 1970 was the first day in Ernie's psychosis. Later that evening, Ernie calmly told Joan he was let go because of cutbacks, and that he was getting a severance package that would be enough for him to buy a taxi plate.

Ernie's older brother Pat was a Taxi Driver and was always bragging about all the money he was making. Joan, throughout their marriage had left all the financial stuff to Ernie, so if Ernie said it was going to be okay, she was happy.

Every Tuesday, like clockwork, Ernie would call up to Percy's house in Rathgar to receive his fifteen pounds.

Occasionally, Percy would get brave enough to say he wasn't going to pay anymore, and that he would go to the guards. Ernie's reply was always the same, "They will be riding that wrinkly awl ass of you in the Joy, Mr Carroll, the cock sucker." Ernie hid the money under the floorboards in the toilet of his house.

One evening while returning from Percy's house, Ernie got a flag-down from a young woman outside Saint Luke's Hospital.

After getting into the back seat, she asked Ernie how much it would be to Blessington in Wicklow. and Ernie checking out his fare card replied, "Twenty-five, but I'll do it for twenty."She nodded her head, and said through sobs and tears, "Okay that's fine." He looked at her in his rear-view mirror and could see she was wearing a cruci-fix over her buttoned-up dress and that she was visibly upset.

"Are you okay?" he asked her. She replied that her mum had just died. So, Ernie reached into his glove com-partment and took out a set of rosary beads that Jesus, driver 34 gave him.

"Would you like to say a prayer for her?" he asked, as he handed her the set of rosary beads.

"You are so kind, I'm Margret, please forgive me, you must have been sent by the angels," she said as she took the beads from him and started to pray.

By the time they got to Blessington, she had revealed her life's story to Ernie, even the part that she was still a virgin, apologising every couple of minutes for her unla-dylike behaviour. Outside the farmhouse, she paid Ernie and asked him if he would like a cup of tea for the road.

Three hours later, Ernie left the farmhouse and re-turned almost every Tuesday for four months.

Margret fell quick and hard for Ernie; for her he was the perfect gentleman, and they had so many things in common. Ernie was an only child and his parents died when he was ten; he told her the story of how he played his clarinet to feed himself. Clearly, he was enjoying the attention and admiration he was receiving thanks to the stories he was making up, like how he was looking after his old bed-ridden aunt in her eighties, trying desperately to keep a roof over her head while driving a taxi and doing gigs around Ireland playing his clarinet.

On Margaret's birthday Ernie told her, he loved her, and that she was the only woman for him. Margret had constantly told Ernie she wouldn't sleep with a man until she was married, but that night they made love for the first time, and unlike the usual sex life that he and Joan had, sex with Margret was passionate and exciting so much that he felt like he was a teenager again.

Over the months, Margret became sexually insatiable, adventurous, and curious. Ernie was loving every moment, until Margret became pregnant. Margret had convinced herself that Ernie would leave her because she was in the family way, so she didn't tell him until she was six months gone; expecting Ernie to run, she eventually told him. Margret was in disbelief and shock when Ernie replied, "Let's get married." Little did she know Ernie was even more shocked he said it.

The wedding was organized very quickly, and within weeks they were standing in the church in Blessington, surrounded by a few friends from Margret's side and obviously no-one from Ernie's.

Every time he visited Margaret, Ernie removed the taxi radio from his car, so she had no way of contacting him when he left for work. While Margret wanted to use her money to pay for Ernie's aunts medical care, Ernie wouldn't hear of it; in fact, he would always become very defensive and upset, saying, that he wanted to be a good man and not have a woman keep him.

Eventually, Margret accepted this quirk about Ernie, that she secretly found very much endearing.

With Ernie staying with his ailing aunt two to three nights a week and playing his clarinet at the weekends to pay for his aunt's care, Margret was basically on her own. The night she went into labour, she called the local cab company to bring her into Naas Hospital, leaving a note for Ernie on the table to let him know. The next day Ernie walked into Naas Hospital with a big stuffed pink bunny rabbit for his new daughter who he insisted on calling Nellie after Margret's late mother.

To the world, Ernie pretended to forget things and seemed to be very absent minded, but, in reality, he planned everything meticulously.

Birthday's Anniversaries, Christmas, Easters, School teacher meetings, the only thing he couldn't organize was a holiday and that was something Joan kept asking for years.

Therefore, Ernie told Margret that he was going to Germany, that this could be his big break playing for a German band, and he would only be gone about five days, which turned into two weeks with the success of the gig and, of course the trouble with customs coming back. Margret fell pregnant again and the Taxi to Naas Hospital solution, wasn't going to work this time. What was he going to do with Nellie? Eventually, he came up with a plan.

One of his passengers, Lisa, worked part time in Houston station as a cleaner. Ernie had built up a good rapport with her over the years collecting her and bringing her back and forth to work. So, he spun her a story, that his wife was very ill and needed rest, offered to pay her for her time to look after Nellie.

But it happened that while Margret gave birth to Georgiana, Ernie's second daughter, he was busy celebrating his anniversary with Joan.

Mrs Cleary was a senile old woman in her seventies that the drivers from Kilmore Taxis, collected every day from shopping, and brought to her doctors once a week. She had no family and lived alone in her bungalow in Killester. Ernie was always volunteering to do her shopping, a job the rest of the drivers really hated. While everyone thought Ernie was an amazing human being, he was really setting the stage for his story of his ailing aunt, who Margret kept asking to meet for two years.

Ernie had exhausted every excuse.

First, he invented she was a proud woman, later that she had dementia, although he would always assure Margret that his aunt would probably die very soon, and things would finally be normal for them.

But after the birth of their second daughter, Margret insisted on meeting Ernie's only living relative, so Ernie planned every scene, from scattering his clothes over the seats in Mrs Cleary's living room, to posing a picture of himself on her fireplace with his Clarinet. He even bought his favourite chocolate gold grain biscuits with Mrs Cleary's money, together with the weekly bunch of fresh flowers that he took away with him every Monday for Margret.

He informed Mrs Cleary that his wife wanted to meet her, as she had heard so much about her.

Even though, Mrs Cleary couldn't comprehend what he was saying, she agreed to meeting his wife.

The meeting was organised for a Sunday morning and after Mass, Ernie, Margret, and the kids left Blessington for Killester, arriving over around eleven am.

Outside the house, Ernie said, he would go in and make sure she wasn't having one of her episodes, because he didn't want to frighten the kids. Actually, what he was really checking was that Mrs Cleary wasn't lucid.

When Margret walked into the bungalow she got a distinct smell of urine, that Ernie left deliberately knowing that his wife hated the smell of urine. The kids started crying and once inside the living room, she finally set eyes on the aunt sitting in a seat while Ernie was placing a blanket over her legs to keep her warm.

Raising the kids up in her arms, Margret said, "These are your great Nieces, Nellie and Georgiana." Mrs Cleary was lucid and after looking at Margret she asked who the bloody hell she was, and what was she doing in her living room.

Then, she started to scream for help; Ernie rushed over trying to calm her down, and Margret retreated to the fireplace, picked up a picture of Ernie, and brought it over to her, and said, "I'm Ernie's wife, see, that's Ernie when he was a small boy, you remember Ernie don't you?"

Mrs Clearly screamed, "Who the hell is Ernie? get out of my house, get out." Over the cries of the kids, Ernie told Margret to bring the kids back to the car while he would settle her down.

As soon as Margret left, Ernie gave Mrs Cleary two sedatives and within a few minutes she was back confused and muddled again, talking to her dead husband Hector.

Twenty minutes later, Ernie returned to the car, saying that she was fine, and that he had to clean her up. On the way back home, Margret told Ernie that his aunt needed professional help and that she never knew what he was dealing with until today. Leaning over to him she kissed his face and said, "God, you are so, so wonderful, so thoughtful, I'm so lucky."

After that day, Margret never mentioned visiting Ernie's aunt but always gave him a basket of fruit and freshly made scones for that he duly charged Mrs Clearly for. For the next years, Ernie lived a perfect double life, fathering two more children with Margret, another daughter called Margret and a son named Timothy Ernie. Margret wanted to call him Ernie, little did she know Ernie's eldest son with Joan was also called after him.

In the meantime, Joan thought she had gone through her menopause and stopped taking contraception.

However, two months later the doctor told her she was pregnant, and Ernie immediately saw the advantage which this new situation brought to him. Joan was going to have to give up work, which meant he had to work longer away from home. By the time Janice was born, Ernie and Joan were almost strangers; he only ever came home to sleep for a couple of hours and then back to work, always complaining that they needed every penny with a new baby. What Ernie didn't plan for was Percy dying.

Coincidentally, on the day of his funeral Ernie called over to his house expecting his money, which was raised to twenty-five pounds at that stage. Percy's wife walked over in her black mourning dress to him, and slapped him across the face, shouting, "You fucking parasite, he's dead, and you won't get another penny." Percy had left a letter explaining to his wife why Ernie was calling over every week for years.

To compensate for the loss of Percy's money, Ernie started to steal items from Mrs Cleary's home and another elderly woman he helped. Slowly, he stripped them of all their valuables, selling them to a guy he knew in Coolock.

It was the Beethoven piano in Mrs Cleary's front room that proved to be the undoing for Ernie. After placing an ad in the paper, he sold the piano for a quarter of its value. The buyer thought he was getting a bargain, but on the day, he was collecting it, Mrs Cleary begged him not to take her husband's piano, telling him that the Taxi Driver was selling all her jewellery. Ernie tried to cover it up by saying, "don't be silly, aunty, I'm Ernie your nephew."
As the buyer became more suspicious, he said he was going to check with the guards. Ernie, panicked and offered him the piano for nothing, saying, "Just take it, its junk, she is senile and doesn't even know her own name."

Later that evening, the buyer informed the police in Coolock station of his suspicions, and Ernie went missing. Nobody thought anything of it, apart from Joan, who eventually rang the guards in Coolock to report him missing.

The detective she spoke to on the phone was an old school friend of her husband and knew Ernie was a person of interest regarding the theft from a house in Killester and the Clontarf. The police in Blessington received the registration of Ernie's Taxi and called up to the farmhouse looking for him.

When she saw the police car driving up the driveway, Margret thought something had happened to Ernie. Standing and shaking she asked them if Ernie was okay; both Cops assured her he was okay and that it was a routine inquiry, asking her to tell Ernie to contact them when he returned home.

An hour later, one of the Cops from Blessington police station phoned Coolock station and spoke to the detective handling the case, who proved to be the same one that knew Ernie. He answered, "Hello, this is detective John Norfick, how can I help you?"

The Cop from Blessington filled him in on their visit to Ernie's house and that they spoke to his wife. John was confused and asked the Cop, "Why he was knocking on a door in Kilbarrack when he was stationed in Blessington?" The Cop replied, "No, I called up to Margret, his wife, they have four kids and live in a farmhouse just off the Blessington Road, have done for years."

John took down the address of the farmhouse and left the police station. He drove straight to Blessington.

When he knocked on the door of the farmhouse, Margret answered, after identifying himself as a detective from the fraud squad, he asked if he could have a private word away from the kids. Margret was getting worried and as she showed him into the front room, John asked her how long they were married and where they got married.

He showed her a picture of Ernie and asked her, "Is this your husband?" Margret froze and knew this wasn't a normal thing to ask.

"Are you going to tell me what is going on? Is my husband in some sort of trouble? Why are you asking me where we got married? If you are from the fraud squad, what's that got to do with anything?"

John replied, "Look, I don't know how to say this, but I'm investigating multiple counts of burglaries in Killester and the Clontarf area, and we need to speak to your husband to assist us in our inquiries." He asked Margret if he could look around the house; still in shock she agreed. After checking to see Ernie wasn't hiding, he saw a picture of Ernie with Margret and the kids and asked Margret if he could take it, promising her that it would be returned. Then, John left and drove straight to Joan's house in Kilbarrack.

As he walked up to her door, Joan ran out sobbing, screaming, "Is he dead? please don't tell me he's dead." John told her he was ok and that he needed to talk to her privately. Joan brought him into the Pallor, and John sat down looking at Ernie's and Joan's wedding photo proudly displayed on the cabinet.

Despite the fact John was a seasoned police officer, this was a first, and he didn't know how to tell her.

"Look I have some news."

The moment he said that Joan started to cry again and said, "You said he wasn't dead."

John replied, "We don't know, and that's the truth."

Joan looked up at him and replied, "Then why are you here? tell me!"

John replied, "There is no easy way of telling you this so, I'm sorry Joan, but Ernie has another family with four kids with a woman he married ten years ago."

Joan started to laugh and said, "Are you winding me up? fuckoff with yeh." She looked at John, who had the picture of Ernie and his family still in his hand.

Joan grabbed the picture, screaming, "Who's this fucking whore? I'll fucken kill him, four fucken kids, oh my Jesus, four kids."

The reality was hitting Joan, she collapsed into the seat and started to cry inconsolably. John asked her when was the last time she had seen Ernie, and she replied that he came into the house four days ago, went up to the bathroom, came back down, and left.

"I thought he just needed the toilet."

John asked her if he could look at the bathroom, Joan nodded through her tears, so John walked up the stairs and into the bathroom. Closing the door, he looked around the room banging on the wooden screen, then he noticed part of the Lino had a crease in the corner of the room. Pulling it back he saw a loose floorboard and lifted it up. There, resting on the board it was hidden a white envelope addressed to Joan. He picked it up and brought it down to Joan, saying, "I found this up in the bathroom."

Joan took the envelope and said, "That's his handwriting." Still crying she opened the letter, and after reading it, she collapsed back into the seat crying once again. The letter fell onto the floor, John picked it up, and read it.

Dear Joan,

If you're reading this, you already hate me, and I understand why. I hate myself; I have no way of explaining to you how this happened, I just snapped and before I knew it, I was married to Margret and she had my kids. You will find this impossible to believe, but I love you both, and never ever wanted to hurt either of you. I knew this day would come, it's a release to be honest. Everyday living in fear of exposure, lying until I didn't know the truth. It mentally exhausted me.

I don't ask for your forgiveness, because I don't deserve it, but I will ask you to tell the kids I love them and will always carry them in my heart.

Yours, forever,

Ernie

After reading the letter, John, asked Joan if he could take it with him, promising to bring it back. Joan, replied, "Burn it, I don't want anything from that bastard."

When Margret was told the truth, she just cried, telling the Cops that she missed her Ernie. Ernie's taxi was found in Dun Loaghaire, his shoes and socks and two wedding rings with buttercups were left beside the shoreline.

The newspapers ran the story for weeks, "love and suicide." Reporters camped outside Joan's house and Margret's farm, pictures of the ten kids and Ernie who they nicknamed the "Taxi Bigamist" was front page.

They interviewed neighbours and friends, Taxi Drivers from Kilmore Taxis, every one of them had the same thing to say, "They never would have believed it possible of Ernie."

The Cops believed Ernie committed suicide and the tide took out his body, the case was closed.

Two years later, Margret opened her front door to find Ernie standing, smiling, asking her if she missed him.

Benny Big Shillings

Back in the eighties, Driver 5, aka, Benny Big Shillings, was a narcissistic sadistic loan shark, despised by his fellow drivers and particularly by John, the Base controller. In his late thirties, he was the son of a notorious criminal gang leader, Dini Boy Briscoe.

For that, Benny used his connections to intimidate his prey, which usually were young struggling mothers and driving a taxi gave him the perfect position. His favourite play was to sucker them in. On a rainy day, Benny would park outside the social welfare clinic offering a free taxi to the mothers carrying their babies, saying it would break his heart to see a baby getting wet.

Alternatively, while dropping them off from the Shopping Centre, he would tell them that if they wanted a loan, he could organise it, complimenting them, and suggesting that they should be wearing a new dress and have their hair done pretty.

"Sure, your children's allowance would pay for it."
By the third or fourth time, he always got them hooked and in time, he had built up a large black book of clients split into two sections, payers, and pro's as he called them.

As soon as one of the young mothers couldn't pay the loan back with one hundred percent interest by the end of three months, he would call up to their house, always after their husbands went to work and threaten them that their spouses would have their legs broken, if they didn't pay.

Most chose not to tell their husbands about the loan so the story would usually end with the petrified young mother offering herself to him. It would start with him riding them or getting a blow job to prevent the assault of their husbands, but once introduced to an alternative way to pay, he would use the willing ones as livestock for his mates to ride, charging them twenty pound per fuck, and making a fortune.

Any woman who threatened to tell the Cops or refused his kind offer found, would soon find their husbands legs broken and labelled a grass.

The men who flocked to Benny were married older guys who wanted to fuck a clean young-one and usually it was junkies who serviced their needs. Benny had a stable of young mothers, some as young as seventeen.

Moreover, as soon as the punter was in the saddle and doing the nasty, as he called it, Benny took photos of them with his polaroid camera in order to blackmail his "Jockeys;" it was a money-making machine with endless clients.

Ram Jam had crossed paths with Benny a few times, on every occasion to the disadvantage and annoyance of Ram Jam, who hated him with a vengeance. As a matter of fact, Benny's fathers' connections meant Ram Jam was powerless to take him on. However, that all changed with the new relationship Ram Jam had with the IRA.

Ram Jams' niece, Sophie, told him that her friend Claudia owed Benny Big Shillings three hundred quid, and he was riding her every day as interest on the loan. She asked Ram Jam for the money and to ask Benny to stop as her friend Claudia was black and blue from the beatings he was giving her.

Normally, Ram Jam wouldn't interfere, but because of his hatred for Benny and the fact he was raping local women, he felt obligated to step up. So, two days later, as Benny was raping Claudia in her bedroom, Ram Jam ran in. Wearing a balaclava and carrying a baseball bat, he knocked the shit out of Benny. With every stroke he said, "Do you know who I am?" and Ram Jam replied in his disguised voice, "Mr broken bones" and smashed another bone in Benny's body.

As Benny lay in a pool of his blood, he blurted out, "You're a dead man." Ram Jam cracked him over the head once again, Benny, unconscious, hit the ground hard. Because of Claudia, Ram Jam didn't kill him, and that was going to be a mistake he would live to regret. Ram Jam told her to get dressed, pack a suitcase, and leave Dublin with her husband, Trevor. He handed her a roll of twenties and said, "Tell your hubby, that Benny's father is head of the Briscoe gang, and Benny broke-in and raped you, forget about going to the police, their all on Briscoe's payroll."

It took months for Benny to walk again, and he still found it hard to select certain words. His father had feelers out everywhere, looking for the couple as they thought it was the husband who left Benny for dead.

It was nearly a year later when one of the Briscoe gang was on a dirty weekend in Tramore with his bit on the side, that he saw Claudia and her hubby in a restaurant and in order to discover their address he followed them back to their apartment on Strand street terrace.

Two nights later, their apartment door was kicked in, Trevor was tortured for three hours in front of Claudia, who was gagged and tied to a chair, and when he didn't admit battering Benny, he was shot in front of her.

As Trevor's body lay on the white carpet, his blood like a silhouette increased around his body, Benny and his accomplices turned their attention to Claudia, first taking turns raping her, promising her, they would stop if she gave up a name.

Hysterical and crying uncontrollably, her eyes transfixed on her husband, she muttered Sophie's name. Benny tried to say, "Now that wasn't difficult," but instead said, "now, that was differential." The rest of the gang laughed at him, Benny took his gun, placed it at the back of Claudia's head, said "Bitch," and blew her brains out. She fell lifeless on top of Trevor's body. Benny turned and said, "She heard that!"

Then, he lifted a can of petrol from the floor that they brought with them and poured the petrol over the bodies, lighting a match as he and his gang left the apartment. Within seconds fire spread through the apartment, alarms and sirens started screeching, while other occupants were scrambling to get out. Benny calmly got into his BMW, looked up at the burning building and smiled.

By the time they got back to Dublin, it was five am. Sophie woke up to find Benny looking down at her, his fingers across his lips, as he put a gun to her head.

"Please don't touch my kids," Sophie pleaded as she walked in front of them down the stairs. She tried to run into the kitchen, but one of the gang members grabbed her, forcing her into a seat.

Benny took off his balaclava, Sophie's face went white, "That's good, you know who I am," Benny said, as he grabbed Sophie by the throat, "You are going to tell me who," again Benny's words came out wrong, "who did me" one of the gang laughed.

Benny hit him in the face with a punch, turning around, he took out some polaroid's he had taken in Tramore, holding them in front of Sophie, he said, "See what happens to rats."

One of the pictures depicted Trevor's body and Claudia being raped, he bent down to her face and said, "Who bathed me?" again mixing up his words, this time, nobody laughed.

Sophie didn't say a word, Benny turned to one of his gang and said, "Bring down the eleven-year-old, want to fuck her." Sophie began to scream and begged Benny not to, that she didn't know what he was talking about, she swore to God, and on her kid's lives, she didn't know anything. Benny shouted, "Get her."

Sophie screamed into his face, "Do you know who my uncle is, he is going to fucking kill you." Benny still hadn't put two and two together, and replied, "He's no buddy, body" he shouted.

Just then, the gang member returned with Sophie's, daughter who was screaming. Sophie shouted, "It was my uncle, he hit you."

Benny told his mate to bring the young-one back up the stairs and grabbed Sophie by the hair slamming her face to the ground, he took a knife and slowly engraved his name on her back, Sophie's screams woke her neighbours, as he left, he told her, "I will be back."

It was 7 am when one of Sophie's neighbours called John in the Base and filled him in on what went down in Sophie's house. John had a phone number for Ram Jam and knew exactly what his friend would do if he told him exactly what had happened to Sophie. Nevertheless, he called the number. It took a dozen rings but eventually

Ram Jam answered, and John told him, "There's trouble, get down to the Base now."

Fifteen minutes later, John filled Ram Jam on what happened. As predicted Ram Jam said he was going to kill Benny, and his fucking crew.

But as he was leaving John grabbed him and said, "They will be expecting you, that's what they want, let's be smart." John was reared in Belfast and knew exactly the trouble that was about to unfold, so he turned to Ram Jam and said, "Let's keep this isolated.

If you react straight away its going to be war, that's no good for business and our health."

Ram Jam responded by shouting right into John's face, "That fucker is dead, I want him fucking dead!"

"Let's call the Fixer and see what he advises, you know he will sort this out," John replied calmly.

Ram Jam left in John's car knowing Benny was looking for him. He went straight up to the Mater Hospital to see his niece, and as he scanned the emergency room, he saw one of Benny's guys with his back to him.

Picking up a fire extinguisher, Ram Jam hit him full force in the face with it, and then walked calmly into the main hospital where he found Sophie. Her hospital gown covered up the worst part of the assault, her eyes were swollen, her face was busted. She told Ram Jam about the pictures of Claudia and Trevor.

Three hours later, John and Ram Jam walked into the Barry house in Finglas, a known IRA hangout, where the Fixer was sitting talking to three guys. One of them Ram Jam knew; the Fixer got up and said, "Let's go outside" pointing to the back door.

Once outside, he asked Ram Jam if he done Benny over. Ram Jam knew better than to lie and told him why.

The Fixer walked back into the pub, John and Ram Jam, looked at each other confused; Ram Jam broke the silence by saying "if he was going to kill us, we would be dead already." John looked at Ram Jam and said "Us."

The two walked back in and over to the table where the Fixer was sitting having a club orange, he looked up at Ram Jam and said, "Go on a holiday."

Ram Jam tried to say he wasn't going to, but the Fixer from thin air produced a knife and stuck it into Ram Jams thigh, "I said take a holiday."

Ram Jam wincing in pain replied, "Yes I will, straight away."

John helped Ram Jam into his car and was about to go to the hospital until Ram Jam said, "No hospitals, I will stitch it myself;" he knew what he was doing, he didn't hit a thing other than fat.

John for the first time since they left the Barry House asked Ram Jam, "Are you really going on a holiday?"

Ram Jam replied, "I know what will happen if I don't."

Considering how mentally restricted Benny and his father were, the Fixer knew exactly where they were going to hit, Ram Jams mother's house, so he ordered his lieutenant known as Hawk to wait out in the back of a van, just down from Ram Jam's mother's house.

Like clockwork Dini, Benny and two guans drove into the estate, once they passed the van, Hawk stood out with a rocket launcher over his shoulder, aimed it at a parked car, and launched the rocket.

Then, he quickly disappeared back into the van. The parked car lifted off the ground and exploded, smashing every windscreen and window, including the car Benny and his father were in.

Cars and house alarms started screeching, neighbours were coming out their houses. Dini knew exactly what had happened, with his ears still ringing he shouted to Benny, "Let's get the fuck out of here!" They abandoned the stolen car shortly afterwards in Stoneybatter, and walked over the hill next to their home, where two parked cars exploded three hundred meters from them, again smashing every piece of glass, with house and car alarms screaming. Benny and his father were pushed to the ground by the force of the blast; the Cops in Cabra received an IRA coded double X message telling them that the bombs were warnings against legitimate targets, and the private cars of police officers from Cabra station were targeted.

Tilt fuses were found under the cars of four members of *Cabra An Garda Siochanna*, nobody knew the significance of the four that seemed to be picked randomly except for Benny's father. Now, they were on his payroll, the IRA was telling him they knew everything, and could get to them anywhere or anytime. Dini also knew he had a IRA mole in his inner circle, nobody else knew the names of the Cops on the take.

Two Armalite AR-10 bullets was posted to Dini's home the next day, while Dini considered himself invincible, he knew as did every Dublin criminal, never to mess with the IRA.

Two days later, Dini's trusted second in command, called Al, walked into a crowded Barry House and placed the two bullets on the counter, and ordered a pint.

Then, he picked up one of the bullets and asked the barman if he could talk to the owner of that.

A guy sitting next to the entrance steel door got up and locked it, while two guys appeared either side of Al, one placing a Armalite rifle on the counter, the other putting a Webley pistol to AL's head.

In a staunch Bogside accent, the one holding the pistol after pressing the weapon harder against AL's head said, "Are Yee working for the flaming lost and found mate?"

Unfazed, Al slowly turned around, the gun now against his temple, and said, without looking up, "I'm looking to call a cease fire on behalf of the Briscoe Gang, mate."

In response, Al's face was hit with the butt end of the Riffle, which knocked him unconscious.

When he woke up, he couldn't move his hands or legs, and immediately realised he was in the back of a parked van with a hood over his head. But the door slid open, someone got in, and in Dublin accent said, "This is our terms, you go back and tell Dini boy, nobody touches our people, nobody.

He drops five percent a week to us from his drug business, sends twenty grand to that little girl Benny engraved and Benny gives up messing with local women, if these terms are not met, all of Yee, will be eliminated."

The door opened again, the guy got out, and the vans engine started.

Fifteen minutes later the door of the van opened, and Al was thrown out onto the Ballyfermot Road, his body hitting the road hard as he bounced across the concrete.

That evening, Al repeated the terms to Dini boy.

Both men knew they had no option, so they both agreed, as they had witnessed first-hand what the IRA had done to the Jennings gangs; taking out one of the bottom feeders and used his coffin filled with Semtex to wipe out the entire gang plus five innocent mourners, at his funeral. "You can't fuck about with the IRA," AL said aloud. Dini nodded and replied, "So it's agreed."

Yet, Benny didn't want to give up his playthings and refused point-blank. Dini ordered him to stand down from fucking the livestock and to hand over his black book to Al, but, two weeks later, while the Briscoe gang had made two payments to the cause and had donated twenty grand to Sophie, Benny was still defying both his father and the IRA.

One day, as Benny left the house of his latest horse as he referred to her, a blue HiAce van pulled up.

Two masked guys grabbed Benny and dragged him into the back of the van, and once inside a northern accent shouted into Benny's ear, "This is your last warning, now is it going to be your balls or a knee cap."

Benny cried like a bitch, and sniffling he said, "Please don't shoot me, I beg you."

The guy didn't wait and shot Benny behind the knee-cap. Benny's screams muffled the sound of the engine, as the other masked guy opened the door with the van still moving, grabbed a sobbing Benny, and said, "Next time your fucken dead," and threw him out of the Van.

Even so, within a month, Benny was out of the hospital and back to his old tricks. According to him, being shot gave him status as he referred to it; his ego was so inflated that he ignored all the warnings from his father and friends and started carrying a Glock with which he enjoyed threatening a few mothers while they were fucking him.

Six months later, Ram Jam returned from Manchester to find his car untouched, however, as a precaution, he knelt down to check it for incendiary devices, and booby traps. He found nothing. He also looked to see if the doors were wired, nothing, he opened the bonnet to check the engine for any strange objects, again nothing, under the seats for pressure pads, still nothing.

So, he sat in and started the engine, turned on the taxi radio and heard John's voice. He called in not mentioning his driver number in case Benny was on the air, "Back in the city."

Recognising the voice, John replied, "Well, welcome back, you were certainly missed, do you think that medical matter is sorted for your uncle?"

Ram Jam replied, "Not certain, but my big brother assures me it is." As a matter of fact, Ram Jam was fully aware of what went down in his absence.

His first call was to Sophie, to ask if he could stay for a bit, in the new house she bought in Lusk with the twenty thousand she received and a little extra from Ram Jam. In a quiet rural country setting her new home sat on an acre of land just outside the village. You could see anyone coming for miles, which gave Ram Jam comfort.

Under his seat he had two Uzi machine guns and an Ak-47. Sophie came out to greet him as he stood out.

Hugging him, she looked up and asked if it was all over. Ram Jam replied he was told it was, "But you know that crazy bastard Benny."

Later, John met up with Ram Jam and filled him in on Benny's movements and that he was running his business as usual. "A local girl was taken to the hospital, he battered her to an inch of her life, Cops were involved but she said she couldn't remember."

During his friend's absence, John had kept a diary of all the places and times Benny stepped out and returned from when he was supposedly working in his taxi, also where he liked to eat and take a break.

John handed Ram Jam the piece of paper and said, "This might come in handy."

Ram Jam smiled as he took it and said, "I hope not."

For three weeks everything was fine, but one evening when out working, Ram Jam picked up two guys on Talbot Street, who said they were going to Cabra. Ram Jam instinctually knew they were not local to Cabra, so he asked them where they were from. One said Inchicore the other Crumlin.

Ram Jam got a bad feeling and blew into John that he might see Charlie in Cabra, Charlie his uncle.

John knew straightaway what he meant, and phoned the Barry House, telling who ever answered a unit member was in trouble in Cabra, giving Ram Jams location and the route he was taking, the make and colour of his car. Within two minutes, a Honda CBR 1000 left the Barry House at speed heading for Cabra.

Ram Jam had trapped his mic open so John could hear everything that was happening in his car. If Ram Jam was passing a pub, he would mention the name so John knew exactly where he was.

Through his rear-view mirror Ram Jam saw one of the guys nodding to the other then taking a large knife out from under his jacket.

"What the fuck are you doing with that knife?" Ram Jam shouted as he slammed the car into second gear, coming up hard off the clutch, jumping on the brake pedal, and sending both guys flying into the front seats.

In seconds, Ram Jam was out of his car.

One of the guys jumped out, took out a gun, and fired at Ram Jam, hitting him in the back, he went down.

John heard the bang and knew it was a gunshot. Then, he heard the other guy turning to his accomplice, "Thought this was supposed to look like a Taxi hijacking gone wrong."

The CBR came down Fassaugh Avenue just as one of the guys pointed his gun at Ram Jam who was lying face down on the concrete and about to be killed.

The motorcyclist sprayed the guy with Uzi machine fire, killing him instantly. The second guy, on the other hand, just put up his hands and kneeled on the ground.

After that, the motorcyclist got off his bike and walked over to see if Ram Jam was still alive. He was.

Then, he turned to the guy still kneeling, and placed the machine gun nozzle, that was still burning hot, to the back of his head and asked, "Who sent you?"

The moment he replied, "Benny Briscoe," the trigger was pressed, and his head exploded like a watermelon, sending blood and brains everywhere. The biker calmly got back onto his bike and disappeared.

When he heard the gunshot, John had left the Base and was driving up to Cabra.

By the time he arrived onto Fassaugh Avenue, Cops and ambulances were already everywhere. From his position, he could see Ram Jam sitting up on a stretcher; he gave him the thumbs up.

Back to the Base he apologised for the break in communication and explained to the drivers, that a fuse blew so there was no electricity for a bit.

He knew Benny was sitting on the Mater Hospital taxi rank with two other drivers giving him the perfect Alibi if he was questioned.

John said over the airwaves, "Lads, Driver 9 was involved in a hijack, he was shot in the back, I'm told he is in surgery and is expected to make a full recovery, his two assailants were not so lucky, they were shot dead by some guy on a motorbike."

Benny immediately threw up. The other drivers asked him if he was alright, but Benny completely lost it, he took out his Glock and pointing it at the stunned drivers, shouted, "I'll fucking kill you!" and he got out driving off the taxi rank at speed.

After the drivers told him what happened, John called driver 5, "Are you okay?" Benny didn't reply.

Ram Jam spent eight hours in surgery because the bullet was lodged in the Rhomboid muscle just below his shoulder blade.

Meanwhile, John kept ringing the hospital claiming to be Ram Jam's brother, until he was told Ram Jam was out of surgery and despite the long road of rehabilitation ahead of him, he should make a full recovery.

John proudly and promptly told the lads, who cheered and applauded their colleague.

After the incident, Hawk and two members of the Finglas Unit of the IRA were parked outside Benny's house for days, while another unit was deployed to known haunts of Benny's.

Anyhow, nobody other than Dini, knew, that Benny was smuggled out of Dublin in a container lorry headed to Spain. Dini knew he would have to make restitution for Benny's reckless actions that placed his entire family at risk.

Two days later, Dini and Al walked into the Barry House, carrying a sports bag.

Just like the last time, the entrance door was immediately locked behind them. They ordered two pints of Guinness and asked the barman if the manager of special events was around. The barman pointed to a black steel door in the corner of the building, so they both got up and walked over.

AL opened the door which led to a big stock room filled with wooden crates that they presumed were weapons and explosives. A guy in a balaclava waved them over, frisked them, and after checking the bag, he told them "To sit there" pointing to two seats that had blood-stained rope hanging from its legs and arms.

Al turned to Dini and said, "I don't think this was a good idea." Dini was just about to reply when the Hawk walked in, and while staring at the two men he put a pipe bomb on the table. Without saying a word, Dini stared back at him while Al focused on the pipe bomb.

Din Boy broke the silence by saying, "Are you trying to intimidate us?"

The Hawk bent down to him and said, "If we wanted to do that, we would've blown up your daughters hair salon in Francis Street, with her wee young un's."

Nobody knew about Dini's estranged daughter, who he hadn't spoken to for ten years so naturally, Dini's face showed obvious signs of shock.

Nevertheless, the Hawk continued, "This is what's going to happen, you give up your son Benny, and the rest of your family will be spared, simple as that."

Then, Dini spoke for the first time, "I didn't sanction any hit, nor do I know where he is, I don't want hassle with you guys, and we came here as a sign of respect," he lifted the bag and opened it, taking out blocks of twenties he said, "there is one hundred thousand quid here, this is a peace offering."

Both men jumped when they heard a loud bang coming from behind a wall of metal beer barrels at the back of where they were sitting.

Hawk left and went behind the barrels. Dini could hear the voices but couldn't make out what was being said. However, when the Hawk returned, he said, "An extra five percent a week, and if Benny sets foot in Ireland, he's dead." Hawk picked up the bag and said, "That's for our wounded unit member, if anyone looks in his direction, five of yours will be shot."

After that, Dini boy stood up, face to face with the Hawk and said, "Tell your boss he has a deal! Al and Dini went out of the place and were about to open their car, when a guy appeared from the back of it. He stood up with a tin biscuit box, that he had retrieved from under Al's car.

He smiled as he passed them and said, "Your lucky day lads."

In the car on the way back, AL turned to Dini boy and said, "Thought we were goners back there, those are fucking crazy psycho bastards."

"Let's hope this is an end to it," Dini boy replied,

"They know everything, what Cops we have in our pocket, everything about my family, our jobs, our movements, that Rat is feeding them, we have to find him fast, and fucken kill him."

Later that evening Al phoned the Hawk, "Dini boy is paranoid and knows he has a rat in the gang." The Hawk asked him if Dini suspected him. Al laughed, and replied, "That fucken egit is too thick to know, I'm going to set up Bog-eye Conroy."

Al had been tapping Bog-eyes missus big tits, Tessa, every time Bog-eye went on a drug run. He wanted to get rid of her as she was all loved up with him, and had started to put demands on him, threatening to tell Bog-eye as she wanted to be with Al.

Al also told Dini that he had a plan to flush out the rat. He was going to tell each of the ten members of the inner circle that they were going to firebomb the Barry House, giving each of them a different day and time.

"We send a spotter each day to see when they locked it down, and then we have ourselves a rat to fry."

Of course, later, Al phoned the Hawk and filled him in. Three days later the Barry House was turned into a fortress, and that pointed the finger directly at Bog-eye.

While Bog-eye was working alone on his drug run and Al was fucking Tessa, at twelve midnight, a pipe bomb packed with six-inch nails went off in the back of Bog-eye's car blowing him to pieces.

After that, Tessa was blackballed by everyone, which suited Al just fine. Every time that he fucked her, he kept saying, "Give it time, everyone thinks you knew your husband was a rat, but I convinced them you didn't know, otherwise you would be dead, if we are seen together, they will kill the both of us." Which of course was bull-shit as everyone knew Al was fucking her.

Benny surfaced in Mijas in the Costa del Sol in Spain. Within six months he had had enough of the Spanish weather, the local prostitutes, crap food, and wanted to come home. So, he called Dini and pleaded with him to organise his return. Al knew he couldn't tell Hawk be-cause it would be so obvious another rat was informing, so he employed a local journalist, a friend of a friend, to take a picture of Benny and leak it to one of the English tabloids.

Three days later, Benny was pictured on the front of the Globe Newspaper carrying a bag, the headlines read, "Irish Gangster is returning home."

The article announced that Benny had informed a lo-cal woman he was coming back to Ireland to claim his rightful throne.

That put an end to Benny's plan to return to Ireland.

Mermaid Aids

In the late eighties, sexually transmitted diseases, or a burst condom resulting in unwanted pregnancies were the least of the problems for Shirley's girls. HIV and AIDS, the silent but deadly killers were taking the lives of sex workers and gay men throughout Ireland.

This story chronicles the loss and heartache of his, lost friends.

With most of his girls and gay friends now infected with HIV, Shirley's life was spent going back and forth to unit five in James Street Hospital, known as the "Gas chamber," like Auschwitz. Those that went there, had all a painful and agonising death.

Throughout the centuries the demand for sex never diminished, irrespective of the circumstances.

So, whenever one of Shirley's girls passed away, another took her place on Fitzwilliam Square; the vicious circle of young girls addicted to drugs, forced to feed their habit the only way they knew.

It was almost five years since Siobhan stopped calling for Shirley. He thought she had qualified and moved away from "that life," as she called it, until one Sunday morning, in late November, while Shirley was passing Fitzwilliam Square and as always, he looked to see if any of his girls were out working, an image of a woman that looked so familiar to him caught his eye. She stood in darkness, under the branches of the trees sheltered from the streetlights.

Curious, he parked his taxi, got out, and as he walked over, she called out, "Are you looking for business?"

Her unmistakable Blackrock accent identified her immediately.

As he got closer, he called to her, "Is that you Siobhan? It's Vincent."

She stood out from under the branches, the streetlight illuminating her gaunt tissue-less face, and Vincent, now standing beside her, reached out to hug her.

He instantly felt how thin and weightless she was, so he looked at her and said, "Oh my God, Siobhan, you poor thing, I'm so sorry."

Even with the makeup he could see Aids had eroded every part of her; her once beautiful flawless complexion, was now sickly yellow, blood vessels crisscrossed over her face, and her bones protruded from under her skin.

The exquisite perfumes she wore now camouflaged the pungent smell of decay. Tears cascaded down Vincent's face and as he held hers in his hands and kissed her, a car passing by, with drunken youths shouted out the window, "Fucken perverts, scum bags."

Siobhan was the first to speak, "As you can see, I have Aids, they tell me I will be dead before Christmas, so I fuck every bastard to make sure I won't be the only one."

Vincent was stunned, and he replied, "Surely you don't want to infect people deliberately."

Siobhan spat back, "It was a dirty married bastard that rode me bareback and gave me this, one of my rich clients who swore he was clean, paid me an extra two hundred for no rubber, two hundred pounds, that's what my life was worth, so I'm just passing on the present. Isn't it funny? The stupid pathetic fuckers pay me an extra tenner so they can fuck me without a condom, I blow them first, bite their skin to make sure and smile as they fuck me."

Vincent's anger erupted, "You are murdering them Siobhan, what about their wife's or children? they didn't do anything to deserve being infected, how can you live with yourself?"

Siobhan looked into Vincent's face, her eyes lifeless, and replied, "Those bastards deserve it, was it not your great God that prophesied about Sodom and Gomorrah? Well, it's not sulphur and fire that he is raining down on us, it's a disease that slowly eats you alive. Heroin is the only way I can get through another day. I'm dead already, just waiting to be buried, so don't start preaching to me about the innocent, let's say I'm doing God's work, spreading my legs and spreading the word of God."

Vincent couldn't reply and just said he had to go to collect a fare, promising to grab a coffee sometime, he told her that his number hadn't changed, and she could ring Kilmore Taxis to get him.

That was the last time they spoke.

Three weeks later the Base received an envelope addressed to Vincent. Inside there was a letter from Our Lady's Hospice for the dying in Harold's Cross informing him that Siobhan had passed away in her sleep the night before, that she had listed him as her next of kin, and that her belongings had to be collected by Friday or they would be destroyed.

Three hours later, Vincent walked into the morgue of Our Lady's Hospice. The stone building was cold, eight gurneys with sheets covering bodies filled the room.

An assistant came out from the office and asked if he could help him. Vincent mentioned Siobhan's name, the assistant disappeared and returned with a small wooden box, and a letter.

He opened the letter when he got back into his car, her handwriting was neat and cursive. He read:

"Vincent,

My forever loving Shirley, you were the closest thing to family I ever knew. You never judged and were always there for me. How I missed our talks and listening to your voice. If you are reading this, it means that I'm dead. I saved up two hundred pounds that I didn't put up my nose. They're in the wooden box in the lining; hopefully it will be enough to bury me. I would like a mosses basket not a wooden coffin, I always hated them. Don't think I will be with your God, not after all the things I did on this earth. Last we spoke, I was full of hate and scared, I felt a wave of warmth come over me, don't think it was the drugs, so I wrote this letter, don't have any deep meaning words to say, just happy I got to meet you. Take care and never change who you are, for you are a living angel.

All my love Siobhan xxxx

Vincent sat and wept, he picked up the wooden box and opened it. A picture of Siobhan when she was a baby was stuck to the lid, along with her holy communion medal. He peeled back the lining and there he found the two hundred pounds she mentioned.

Three days later, he had organised her funeral, adding over a thousand pounds of his own money to give Siobhan her final request. He got her a mosses basket, and as he stood in the church in Harold's Cross he looked around. He was alone, just him and Siobhan. He tried to contact Gorgeous George, but he was away in Spain on holiday.

Nobody responded to her obituary in the newspaper, that Vincent placed; there was nobody to mourn her, just him.

As they carried her out, an elderly woman came over to Vincent and said in the exact same accent as Siobhan, "Is this Siobhan Jenkins funeral?" Vincent nodded.

She reached out her hand and said, "I am, sorry." She was Siobhan's mother. Vincent looked at her and asked, how she knew it was her Siobhan that died, as they hadn't spoken in over twenty years.

She replied, "My neighbour read her obituary and knew by her age and that she was formally from Blackrock. To be honest, I expected that knock on the door for over twenty years."

Vincent asked her if she wanted a lift to Palmerstown Cemetery, she accepted, and they walked to his taxi. He could see the physical resemblance she shared with Siobhan, same cheek bones and eyes, tall and elegant.

He opened the door for her, and as she sat in, she turned to him and said, "I'm so rude, my name is Margorie," again reaching out her hand.

As Vincent followed the hearse, he asked her, why she was alone, telling her he knew about the stepfather and what he had done to Siobhan.

Margorie became defensive and replied, "I don't know what you are talking about." Vincent calmly turned to her and said as he stopped at a red traffic light, "I used to be a priest, please don't lie to me."

277

Even though he was no longer a priest, Irish people still considered former priests in the same light, particularly older people, so lying to them, was akin to lying to God.

"I held your daughter as she revealed her darkest secrets to me, I know what he did and that you knew what he was doing. It doesn't make any difference now. Siobhan is gone, so there is no need to lie and disrespect the dead. Nobody will be pointing any fingers, your secret died with her."

Margorie asked him if Siobhan and he were together. Vincent smiled and replied, "No, I'm gay, I carried Siobhan in my taxi, we became very good friends."

Changing the subject, he asked her, "What happened to Siobhan's auntie Bernie and Phyliss from next door? she was always talking about them."

"Both, sadly, passed away," Margorie replied still looking at the hearse in front of her, flowers in the back window spelt out Siobhan's name.

"Who paid for the funeral?" Margorie asked Vincent. He replied, "Siobhan."

As they entered Palmerstown Cemetery Vincent noticed Dipso Debbie and the Duce. Both had flowers in their hands; it was the first time in ten years he had ever seen them in daylight.

The four of them stood around the grave as the Priest blessed the ground and gave another mass. When the Duce laid her flower on Siobhan's Basket she whispered, "Nobody can hurt you anymore, play with the angels, for you are at home with them now. I hope to see you some day."

After the mass, the priest left, Margorie tried to introduce herself to the Duce. She reached out her hand and said, "I was Siobhan's mother."

The Duce replied ignoring her hand, "No real mother would let her child be raped by an animal, you were never a mother."

Margorie stunned said nothing, so, Vincent asked if anyone wanted to go for a drink or tea.
Dipso Debbie was the first to accept, followed by the Duce, but Margorie said she had an errand to do.

She said goodbye to Vincent and left, flagged down a taxi outside the cemetery and was never seen again.

Driver 90 AKA "Miss Ireland"

Angela was forty-eight years old and a female Taxi Driver, which back then was a rarity. Brought up in the north-inner city, she had a hard life, with her husband running off with her younger sister and leaving her with five kids to look after.

She was at least six stone overweight for her five-foot two-inch frame; still, she absolutely didn't give a shite what people thought of her and had the worst potty mouth in the Taxi fleet.

Besides, she never used make-up, saying "it was like putting lipstick on a pig." She always wore her trademark cotton brown tracksuit, that had an assortment of stains from kebabs, coffee, and cum, getting washed once a week on Monday night.

Her underwear was visible for all to see, a black girdle and a white platex bra, which hopefully joined the track-suit on wash day; her description, not the first image that comes to mind of a woman who got more propositions from men than Vogue models.

She started work at four AM, just when all the schizos, dispos, and weirdos surfaced from Lesson Street, full of wine, high on something, and gagging for a shag.

Therefore, with most of the working girls at that time of the morning gone home, Angela became a much sought-after commodity.

Her clients ranged from young guys in their twenties, married men in their forties, to old farts in their sixties. They all rang John in the Base, desperately looking for Angela.

"Supply and Demand," she would joke back to John.

281

"Big demand for a pussy, and I have the only supply at this hour in the morning." She charged twenty quid for a wank, forty quid for a ride with a condom, and whatever the taxi meter totalled at the end of the journey.

Her favourite twisted sense of enjoyment was fucking a neighbour's husband in her taxi, charging him for it, and just in case he couldn't remember his drunken fuck, Angela always scraped their asses with her nails as a little reminder so she could mentally torture the husband later.

She loved telling the pretty wives, who she went out of her way to meet, "I picked up your husband the other night in my taxi, God bless him he was drunk, how was his little head the next day!" always with a big smile on her face.

Angela had many clients, they all started the exact same way, flagging her taxi down, getting in beside her, and asking to visit Fitzwilliam Square.

Most of them didn't realise at that moment the driver was a woman; then, with Fitzwilliam Square absent of any prostitutes, their focus immediately turned to Angela.

The majority of them just asked her straight out, if she would like to make an extra couple of quid.

Angela always had the same answer, putting her hands between their legs, saying, "Would you like me to empty your balls?"

Depending on the guy and how desperate he was, she requested payment up front, sometimes asking for fifty pound which was double compared to what the girls on the square got claiming–she wasn't a prostitute and she had very rarely done this.

She loved keying her mic when she got a young guy, as John would be forced to hear her ask him, how old he was, and then with feigned shock, "God, your young enough to be my son," taking out her tits and telling them to suck them like a baby.

John often shared with other drivers Angela's encounters across the airwaves; the sound of some guy pumping Angela and cuming, or Angela giving some guy a hand job, repeating the same sentence, "You're a big boy, now cum for mammy."

Nobody was off limits for Angela, even the parish priest who met her late one night coming home from a seminar, with too many glasses of wine on board, ended up asking her for a ride.

Three minutes later, he was finished, and Angela was fifty quid richer, which led to a long-established arrangement between father Francis and her.

A Christian brother also availed of her services, along with four old Batchelors in their seventies, who under the guise of delivering a food order once a week, met her so she could give them "a hand," as she called it.

Angela got off on trying to embarrass John, telling him she was stepping out for a minute to milk herself an old goat. On her return, she would tell him while laughing, "That old goat was bucking like a fucking good thing, until he popped his cheese spread all over me hand."

The sounds of John cringing with disgust over the airwaves made her day.

Visiting rugby fans were Angela's favourite passengers, coming back from Lesson Street, pissed drunk, away from the girlfriends or wife's, looking for a good time.

One such rugby fan was a guy called Allen from Llandudno, in Wales, separated from his friends who scored some friendly girls in copper face Jacks. Allen wanted some fun too, so he flagged Angela's taxi down, got in, and asked her if she knew any place where he could find a girl.

Angela told him, "God, this is Ireland, those girls are gone home at this stage."

He had the strongest Welsh accent, he looked like he was twenty-seven, over six foot tall, and built like a shite house according to Angela.

When he was propositioning Angela, she keyed her mic so John could hear. In his thick accent he said, "I don't do these things you know; I have a little wife and a Bern at home."

Angela teasing him, said, "If you don't want to it's okay," after all she had his money in her pocket at that stage.

Allen replied, "No, I'll get my pidyn out and we can have us a good old rogering."

Angela didn't understand him, along with John who couldn't follow the conversation. So, Angela asked him, "What's a Pidyn?"

Allen reaching into his trousers took out his cock and said, "It's my willy."

Angela replied, "Is he frightened to see me?"

Her expectations were shattered the moment she saw he had a miniature cock and there was no physical way in a car he could penetrate her with that little thing. So, she started to wank him, Allen said pulled the thing, but Angela thought he said sing to it.

Angela never one for missing a bit of craic pulled his cock harder, and started to sing, "Hi ho, Hi ho, it's off to work we go, I pull all day, until I get my pay."

Allen shouted, "What are you doing mad woman? I'm not a fucken dwarf, and you're definitely not fucken snow white."

Then, he started to cry, and again anything he said through his sobs was totally indecipherable.

Later, he started to violently punch his cock and balls, repeating the only two words Angela understood.

As Allen hit his cock again, he said them over and over, "Dirty Bastard, dirty bastard."

Angela frozen in shock, just kept looking at him, until John broke the silence and said, "Driver 90 do you need Charlie to give you a hand with that situation?"

Passengers Confessions

Women certainly have foresight, whereas men suffer from the burden of hindsight.

Female passengers are usually coy about revealing anything personal to a stranger, their chain of thought being, *this man might have family or friends living near her.*

Most male passengers, on the other hand, usually can't wait to tell a Taxi Driver about their latest sexual exploits. And, with over two hundred thousand passengers carried, most in an inebriated state, this author has heard and seen it all.

Just to show the vast differences between female and male passengers, a Taxi Driver hears and smells everything in his six-foot square box he occupies for ten hours a shift.

When a person gets in with the smell of cum or sweat, that's immediately obvious to the driver, while, ironically when a female passenger gets into a taxi early in the wee small hours, she has already sprayed perfume to camouflage the smell, and she volunteers an excuse that she was up minding her sick auntie, or she got sick earlier, always mindful that this stranger, who is driving her home, might know someone that might know them, or it could be a defence to ward off his advances.

The stark contrast is so obvious with male passengers who instead, don't give a shit or care about how they smell. On the contrary, for them, it's like a badge of honour. Some even offer their fingers to the Taxi Driver to smell. Yes, guys are crude, juvenile, and suffer from the absence of foresightedness.

It might be the strangest confession box, but the back seat of a Taxi, like the salon seat in a hairdressers or stool in a bar, represents the place were strangers pour out their hearts or expose their most intimate secret.

Using a complete stranger as a sounding board, whether it's for entertainment on their side, shock value, or a shoulder to cry on, passengers who get into a taxi, in a matter of ten minutes, are bound to reveal their darkest torment.

Tens of thousands of passengers carried, young, old, gay, straight, married, single; being a Taxi Driver means getting an insight into people's lives like no other job would allow you.

Through your rear-view mirror you can look at that ordinary looking woman, the soccer mum, the neighbour next door, who is now divulging she is pregnant with her sister's husband, revealing her six-year affair and its story confessed to a complete stranger...

A stereotypical female passenger having an affair.
A dutiful husband flags down a taxi that just dropped off a fare in Portmarnock. He told the driver, his wife was going into the Marcushella Bingo Hall in Amiens Street in Dublin's city centre.

The wife appeared from the front door of her house, wearing a big navy unflattering jumper over black jeans, her hair scraped back, no make-up. She was carrying a large bag in hand as her husband kissed her and wished her good luck. Then, he stood waving as the taxi drove away. Two hundred meters into the journey she asked the driver where he was from, he replied "Cavan." She told the driver, "Forget going into town, bring me to Sutton Cross." The driver watched through his rear-view mirror as she retrieved clothes from her bag, changed her clothes discretely, applied make-up, and removed the elastic rubber band that held her hair, letting it cascade around her shoulders. She then proceeded to remove the navy jumper to reveal a silk blouse, of which she opened the top buttons of her blouse, in order to bring out her cleavage now quite obvious. Once taken the jeans off, a little black mini skirt with visible lingerie at the top of her long legs appeared, and after a final check in her mirror and a spritz of her perfume, the transformation was finally completed.

From a house mom to a sex Goddess in six minutes.

As the driver approached Sutton Cross, she directed him into Burrow Road, and asked in her very distinct posh accent how much was the fare. "Three pound and twenty pence" the Taxi Driver replied, disappointed he wasn't getting his return fare to the city. But she asked him if he wanted to pick her up at ten thirty, and to switch on his taxi meter at the Clontarf junction before he picked her up, which was a good five miles from where he was right now. Even so, knowing it was going to be a great taxi fare he agreed, although he was also intrigued by what she was really up to.

As he drove off, he could see in his rear-view mirror George appearing from a house. She threw her arms around him and kissed him passionately.

Later that evening, the Taxi Driver passed Clontarf at ten fifteen, he switched on his meter as directed, and he got to Burrow Road exactly at ten thirty.

She came out and got into the back seat. Her hair all tossed, make-up smudged, clothes all creased, and as the distinct smell of sex filled the car, she delved into her bag of tricks and started with make-up remover. The hair also returned to its original form, followed by the dowdy house moms' clothes. Then, she took out a pen and marked her hand with ink marks.

As the Taxi pulled up outside her home, the driver noticed the husband waiting patiently. She got out of the car, bingo book in hand, pen over her right ear.

The husband asked her, "How did you do tonight my love?" She replied, "I was only waiting on one number" as she walked up the path.

The husband looked into the taxi at the meter and said, "Eleven fifty, that's what it is every week, here's twelve pound keep the change."

Every part of her affair was planned, premeditated, and calculated. The exact fare determined by distance, checking where the driver was from, right down to placing ink marks on her hand, as she supposedly nervously waited for that winning one number; definitely not sixty-nine, she got that one, probably forty-six, "up to tricks."

The foresightedness of female passengers never ceases to amaze. Sounding like a defeatist for my male race but experiencing tens of thousands of guys repeating the same actions, offers an insight.

Sadly, the same cannot be said about male passengers. Guys mainly think with their dicks, regardless of age or social background, whether it's a male macho thing or just stupidity on their part; one thing is for sure, ninety nine percent who get into a taxi after fucking someone, always want to brag or relive their sexual encounter.

"She had bits tits," holding out their hands to simulate the size, "her pussy was so tight, she sucked me dry, she did this, she did that, we fucked like mad things."

Not for one moment do they think that the guy driving them home might have a friend or relative living near them.

Guys have to tell their male friends of their affairs. Ironically, that mythical saying "Women talk" couldn't be any further from the truth. Women value the consequence of their actions so most women wouldn't tell their best friends.

Yet, men are only short of taking out an advertisement on the radio. It's no wonder more women have affairs undetected than men.

While men swear not to tell a living soul not even their best friends, in reality, they are the eyes and ears of their wives or girlfriends, revealing what their male friends are up to. All said in the strictest of confidence, of course.

Guys are exposed to having affairs mainly because of their own blatant stupidity and laziness.

Gorgeous George and the Soccer Mum

George's favourite women were preferably married for over ten years, with two or three kids, because that meant they were on the pill or using some form of contraception, as most didn't want any more children.

George knew the mindset of men, particularly married men, how they become insensitive, inconsiderate, and lazy in the bedroom. For their wives, their sex-lives had become ritual, uneventful, and tedious; a function required to keep their selfish husbands satisfied while the wives' needs and desires remained ignored.

Consequently, those women were left to self-pleasure themselves after their husbands rolled over and went to sleep. George had slept with hundreds of married women, who had repeated the same comment about their husbands, "Fucking bastard just uses me, all about his fucken needs. Foreplay for him is him playing with me for two minutes and then getting up on me, grunt and moan and then he's done, that's supposed to turn you on, wham bam and it's over."

After years of being used and taken for granted, the seed of resentment had subconsciously grown.

George knew exactly how to charm and seduce a woman. Hens nights, fortieth birthday parties, and office nights out, brought plenty of unhappy married women into George's taxi.

Therefore, he was well accustomed to being chatted up by women. But married women were his weakness, forbidden fruit, because as he had learned married women were extremely adventurous and open to exploring their sexual fantasies.

George was always very well dressed, he wore the latest aftershave, and his smile was polished for his modeling work. He was gifted in making every woman he met feel extraordinary special, studying them as they got into his taxi, the curvature of their bodies under their drab economical dresses, once, young girls, now blossomed into beautiful women.

Taken for granted for years had eroded their self-confidence. George's attraction to married women was much deeper than just sex; he yearned to be truly loved.

Raised in a dysfunctional family who never hugged or showed affection, George craved that rarest of things, unconditional love. That's why, married women were for him the oasis of love he so desired.

With his bright wide smile, and stunning blue eyes, he always started with a simple compliment, "I know this sounds quite forward, and I hope you don't mind me saying, but you have captivating eyes."

He usually waited for them to say they were married, so he could say their husband was a lucky guy.

Reverse psychology at work, probably that would be the first compliment they had received in a long time.

He evaluated their reaction or how they physically responded, although their real answer usually was, "I bet a good-looking guy like you has lots of girlfriends, or why would you be interested in me? a married woman."

Those words left the door open for him to say, "Single girls just want to rush to the alter, get engaged, and get married." George always spoke with such sincerity and confidence, about his love for Art, as well as how he found women over thirty to be so alluring and attractive.

Being an amateur artist, he fell in love with Renaissance artists like Calypso, Da Vinci, who painted women in their true form of beauty, not stick tin samples that tv portrayed as the perfect woman. Then, he would go on, and if they seemed interested, he would reveal, that as a teenager, he was attracted to women like, Sophia Loren, Brigitte Bardot, who he considered to be real women, and that he grew up on those images of true beautiful natural women. Besides, he would always end his comments with the same words: "And in case you are wondering, yes I do find you very attractive."

Those who reciprocated the interest in having fun with George usually followed with, "Wow! not what I was expecting" or something along those lines.

Fionnuala a thirty-seven-year-old married woman from Portmarnock flagged George down in Amiens Street. Her two older sisters stood beside her as she got into the back seat.

Margret, her older sister said, "I've got his number, Jesus, did you see him? he's fucking gorgeous, can I go home with him? he can have his way with me anytime."

They all laughed as Fionnuala closed the door and said she was going to Portmarnock, apologising for her sister being a bit of a ticket.

George turned around, smiled at her, and said that he appreciated the compliment.

Fionnuala without thinking said, "My sister wasn't lying."

George replied still smiling at her, "I could say the same about you."

295

Seventeen years of marriage had removed her confidence, and her one and only night out, every week was spent playing bingo with seventy-year-olds.

George could see the form of her curvaceous body under her jumper, her natural beauty. She had exquisite cheekbones and big brown eyes, her clothes were old fashioned and George, thought her husband must be quite old, so he asked her, "What do you do for fun?"

She replied, "My husband is a stamp collector, and we go once a month to a market in Balbriggan to see if we can uncover any good finds."

George smiled and started to laugh, Fionnuala asked him what he was laughing at.

George apologised and said, "It was inappropriate."

She pressed him until he said, "Hope your husband does more than lick stamps."

"Are you flirting with me?" Fionnuala asked.

At the next red traffic light George turned around and said, "Yes I am, by the way my name is George."

"I'm Fionnuala," she replied smiling back at him, her face now red from embarrassment.

"Would you like to grab a coffee sometime?"

George looking at her in his rear-view mirror, saw her looking at her watch, "Not tonight, hubby is a bit of a timekeeper, but I could meet you tomorrow afternoon if you like."

"That sounds great, would you like me to pick you up?" George asked her.

"I go for my walk around two, so if you are around the kiosk along the strand, I will flag you down," Fionnuala answered. Just as George turned onto the Portmarnock strand he asked her, not to stand him up.

She smiled and said, "I was thinking, you, might stand me up."

George pulled over the car and said, "Would you like a kiss goodnight?" So, Fionnuala came in between the two front seats and met George's face.

He kissed her so gently and passionately, his long tongue exploring her mouth, as his fingers stroked the side of her face. She sighed, and after breaking the kiss said, "God, I haven't been kissed like that in years."

As Fionnuala directed him to her house, a guy in his late forties came to George's window, knocked on the glass, and after a peek at the meter he said, "Eleven fifty, that's what it is every week, here's twelve, keep the change."

The next afternoon, George drove down Portmarnock strand at two pm. Fionnuala's hand was in the air at the Kiosk. She was smiling as she got in beside him, and the first thing she said was, "Well George, I have been thinking of that kiss all night."

She asked him where they were going as she had about three hours before her husband got home.

George replied, "Let's go for coffee in Sandymount and see I can improve on that kiss."

They both smiled, and as they drove along the seafront George reached out and caressed the side of Fionnuala's face, gently tipping her neck. George wanted to get to know all her sensual points, but Fionnuala had other ideas, because once they arrived at Dolly Mount Strand, she said, "Pull over here."

Suddenly, her hands were all over George and she was screaming, "Fuck me, fuck me!"

George had keyed his mic for John to hear. Then, he shot back his seat as far as it could go and put his hand around Fionnuala. She straddled him, and pulled off his t-shirt, while her tongue was tracing down his neck and her hands were frantically trying to open his jeans.

George whispered, "Slow down girl," but Fionnuala only screamed back "Yes, fucking yes."

The moment she saw his cock, her hand pulled down her tracksuit pants, and again she screamed, "Fuck me, fuck me!"

George flipped her around onto her back, saying "Well if that's what you want." He penetrated her hard, and she sighed, as George pumped her harder and harder.

Her moans were like screams getting louder with each thrust. A jogger slowed down to look in the window, George just smiled at him. Then, he returned to Fionnuala's mouth, and while sliding down her body, he removed his cock from her pussy.

That's when she shouted at him, "What the fuck are you doing? Give me that cock!"

George again whispered, "Relax, let me taste you."

Before reaching her pussy, he could smell her scent and cum, and feel how much his seat was soaking wet even before putting his hands under her thighs. He opened her legs and started to lick her clit, again Fionnuala started to scream, this time she was talking to God, "oh God, oh God, fuck yes." Her body tightened, and she orgasmed gushing into George's open mouth. He made slurping noises as he vacuumed her pussy, swallowing her cum; her body twitching and pulsating every time he gulped, she slumped into the seat, trying to catch her breath she said, "That was fucking incredible! you are

298

fucking gorgeous, hung like a fucking horse and ride like one, and you give fucking head too, Jesus Christ that's the best ride I've had ever."

George kissed her passionately and asked her, "Would you like to get into the back seat?"
Fionnuala agreed and still with her pants on one leg, her bare ass and wet pussy visible as she manoeuvred between the seats.

George, without a care in the world just got out of the car with his jeans opened, showing off his six-pack to passing motorists. He got into the back seat; the windows were steamed up.

Once inside, he pushed both front seats forward, he sat down, took out his bulging cock and said, "Sit down on that and fuck me." Fionnuala didn't need to be asked twice.

The taxi was rocking up and down, Fionnuala's moans and sighs were like a dog howling, so much so, that a passer-by knocked on the window of the taxi, asking if everything was alright. Fionnuala was still in the cowgirl position as George with a big smile on his face put down the window, and said, "Yes everything is fucking great." The passer-by mortified and not knowing where to look took off.

George smiled at Fionnuala and said, "Where were we?"

"Your fucking mad," she replied with a big smile.

John in the Base nicknamed her Freaky Fionnuala.

She loved having sex outdoors or in the most dangerous place, like in the GPO in O'Connell street when George was dropping her off to go shopping one Saturday afternoon.

299

That day, he needed to make a phone call, so, after saying goodbye to her, he went into the phone room which consisted of a row of wooden kiosks with a door and two tiny glass windows. But the moment George picked up the receiver and started to dial, the door opened and closed, and Fionnuala was now standing beside him. She urgently opened his jeans, took out his hard cock, and said, "Let's fuck in here."

Needless to say, it didn't take too long before Freaky Fionnuala screams of delight ended that quick encounter.

She also possessed a twisted perverse kink about blowing George as he sat on her husband's cellophaned pages of his stamp collection.

On those occasions, she would say, "My husband is a Philatelist, and I love giving fellatio on his penny stamps, he so loves cleaning those fucking pages."

The affair lasted five months until Fionnuala said she wanted to leave her husband for George.

Driver 22, "Buckets Defence"

Buckets had a litany of complaints made against him almost daily from passengers.

Most of them didn't go any further than bending the ear off the Base controller. But some reported him to the Carriage Office that policed the taxi business back then, and that was managed by the Irish Police.

Once, Buckets received notice from the Carriage Office communicating to him that six separate complaints had been filed against him, and all about his behaviour in the month of July.

The first was from a deaf couple who Buckets picked up on the Drumcondra Road at eight pm on the 3rd of July 1985. They alleged Buckets didn't understand them when they told him where they were going. He told them they were fucking drunk and couldn't understand a word they were saying. They tried to tell him they were deaf, but he became aggressive and said they were pissed out of their heads and put them out of his taxi.

The second was committed on the 9th of July 1985 when a male passenger, in a vulnerable state, confided in Buckets that he intended to commit suicide by jumping in front of a number twenty-five bus. The boy claimed Buckets told him to think of the poor Bus Driver and his family, and to commit suicide in his bath after ringing the Beaumont Hospital to donate his organs. Buckets also asked the passenger for all his money stating he wouldn't need it.

The third complaint was from a person in a wheelchair that asked Buckets to place his wheelchair in the boot of his car and Buckets told him, if he couldn't hop in, to wheel the fuck off; stating he didn't get paid for lifting fat fuckers and the passenger needed an ambulance not a taxi.

The fourth was from a priest who claimed Buckets called him a pervert and a transvestite, made a litany of allegations about his person, one being that he was a "fudge fucker."

The fifth one was from a member of the Hare Krishna society claiming Buckets stapled two of their follower's robes together and banged them over their head with their drum.

The final one was the most serious of all.

The passenger claimed Buckets assaulted him while counting his money under his coat. According to him, Buckets smacked him in the face, shouting he was a dirty little pervert wanking himself in his car.

The date of the hearing was August the 5th 1985. Buckets was so impressed by the way Nuts handled the Cops with the Man Eater that he had asked Nuts to represent him at the Hearing…

To be cont.:

INDEX